NNS Framework Year 4

Autumn and Summer

Oral and mental: e.g. counting, mental strategies, rapid recall	34–37, 52–53, 56–63

Unit	Days	Topic	Target Maths pages
1	3	Place value, ordering and rounding Reading numbers from scales	2–4 77
2–3	10	Understanding + and − Mental calculation strategies (+ and −)	28–31 34–37
		Pencil and paper procedures (+ and −)	38–43
		Money and 'real life' problems Making decisions and checking results	70–73 68–71, 125, 36
4–6	13	Measures, including problems	74–90
		Shape and space Reasoning about shapes	91–108 91–108
7	2	**Assess and review**	118–127

Oral and mental: e.g. counting, mental strategies, rapid recall	34–37, 52–53, 56–63

Unit	Days	Topic	Target Maths pages
8	5	Properties of numbers Reasoning about numbers	13, 16–17 11, 44, 69, 101, 124–125
9–10	10	Understanding × and ÷ Mental calculation strategies (× and ÷)	45–48 54–55, 60–63
		Pencil and paper procedures (× and ÷)	64–67
		Money and 'real life' problems Making decisions and checking results	70–73 68–71, 125, 65–67
11	5	Fractions and decimals	18–27, 72–73
12	5	Understanding + and − Mental calculation strategies (+ and −)	28–31 34–37
		Pencil and paper procedures (+ and −)	38–43
		Time, including problems	84–90 88–90
13	5	Handling data	110–117
14	2	**Assess and review**	118–127
Total	60		

Spring

Oral and mental: e.g. counting, mental strategies, rapid recall	34–37, 52–53, 56–63

Unit	Days	Topic	Target Maths pages
1	3	Place value, ordering and rounding Reading numbers from scales	2–4 77
2–3	10	Understanding + and − Mental calculation strategies (+ and −)	28–31 34–37
		Pencil and paper procedures (+ and −)	38–43
		Money and 'real life' problems Making decisions and checking results	70–73 68–71, 125, 36
4–6	13	Measures, including problems	74–90
		Shape and space Reasoning about shapes	91–108 91–108
7	2	**Assess and review**	118–127

Oral and mental: e.g. counting, mental strategies, rapid recall	34–37, 52–53, 56–63

Unit	Days	Topic	Target Maths pages
8	5	Properties of numbers Reasoning about numbers	13, 16–17 11, 44, 69, 101, 124–125
9–10	10	Understanding × and ÷ Mental calculation strategies (× and ÷)	45–48 54–55, 60–63
		Pencil and paper procedures (× and ÷)	64–67
		Money and 'real life' problems Making decisions and checking results	70–73 68–71, 125, 65–67
11	5	Fractions and decimals	18–27, 72–73
12	5	Handling data	110–117
13	2	**Assess and review**	118–127
Total	55		

CW00553167

NNS Guide Year 4

The references are page numbers in Target Maths.

Numbers and the number system

Place value, ordering and rounding (whole numbers)

2–4
- Read and write whole numbers to at least 10 000 in figures and words, and know what each digit represents.
Partition numbers into thousands, hundreds, tens and ones.

6–7
- Add/subtract 1, 10, 100 or 1000 to/from any integer, and count on or back in tens, hundreds or thousands from any whole number up to 10 000

5
- Multiply or divide any integer up to 1000 by 10 (whole-number answers), and understand the effect.
Begin to multiply by 100.

8–9
- Read and write the vocabulary of comparing and ordering numbers. **Use symbols correctly, including less than (<), greater than (>), equals (=).**
Give one or more numbers lying between two given numbers and order a set of whole numbers less than 10 000.

10
12
- Read and write the vocabulary of estimation and approximation. Make and justify estimates up to about 250, and estimate a proportion. **Round any positive integer less than 1000 to the nearest 10 or 100.**

14–15
- Recognise negative numbers in context (e.g. on a number line, on a temperature scale).

Properties of numbers and number sequences

13
- Recognise and extend number sequences formed by counting from any number in steps of constant size, extending beyond zero when counting back: for example, count on in steps of 25 to 500, and then back to, say, −100.

16
- Recognise odd and even numbers up to 1000, and some of their properties, including the outcome of sums or differences of pairs of odd/even numbers.

17
- Recognise multiples of 2, 3, 4, 5 and 10, up to the tenth multiple.

Fractions and decimals

18–21
- Use fraction notation. **Recognise simple fractions that are several parts of a whole,** such as $\frac{2}{3}$ or $\frac{5}{8}$, **and mixed numbers,** such as $5\frac{3}{4}$; **recognise the equivalence of simple fractions** (e.g. fractions equivalent to $\frac{1}{2}$, $\frac{1}{4}$ or $\frac{3}{4}$).
Identify two simple fractions with a total of 1 (e.g. $\frac{3}{10}$ and $\frac{7}{10}$).

21
- Order simple fractions: for example, decide whether fractions such as $\frac{3}{8}$ or $\frac{7}{10}$ are greater or less than one half.

22
- Begin to relate to fractions to division and find simple fractions such as $\frac{1}{2}$, $\frac{1}{4}$, $\frac{1}{5}$, $\frac{1}{10}$ ... of numbers or quantities.
Find fractions such as $\frac{2}{3}$, $\frac{3}{4}$, $\frac{3}{5}$, $\frac{7}{10}$ ... of shapes.

23
- Begin to use ideas of simple proportion: for example, 'one for every...' and 'one in every...'

24–26
72–73
- Understand decimal notation and place value for tenths and hundredths, and use it in context. For example:
order amounts of money;
convert a sum of money such as £13·25 to pence, or a length such as 125 cm to metres;
round a sum of money to the nearest pound.

27
- Recognise the equivalence between the decimal and fraction forms of one half and one quarter, and tenths such as 0·3.

Calculations

Understanding addition and subtraction

28–31
- Consolidate understanding of relationship between + and −.
Understand the principles (not the names) of the commutative and associative laws as they apply or not to addition and subtraction.

Rapid recall of addition and subtraction facts

32–33
- Consolidate knowing by heart:
addition and subtraction facts for all numbers to 20.
Derive quickly:
all number pairs that total 100 (e.g. 62 + 38, 75 + 25, 40 + 60);
all pairs of multiples of 50 with a total of 1000 (e.g. 850 + 150).

Mental calculation strategies (+ and −)

34
- Find a small difference by counting up (e.g. 5003 − 4996).
6
- Count on or back in repeated steps of 1, 10 or 100.
34
- Partition into tens and units, adding the tens first.
35
- Identify near doubles, using known doubles (e.g. 150 + 160).
35
- Add or subtract the nearest multiple of 10, then adjust.
36
- Continue to use the relationship between addition and subtraction.
36
- Add 3 or 4 small numbers, finding pairs totalling 10, or 9 or 11. Add three two-digit multiples of 10, such as 40 + 70 + 50.
37
- **Use known number facts and place value to add or subtract mentally, including any pair of two-digit whole numbers.**

Pencil and paper procedures (+ and −)

38–43
- Use informal pencil and paper methods to support, record or explain additions/subtractions.
Develop and refine written methods for:
column addition and subtraction of two whole numbers less than 1000, and addition of more than two such numbers;
money calculations (for example, £7·85 ± £3·49).

Understanding multiplication and division

45–48
- Extend understanding of the operations of × and ÷, and their relationship to each other and to + and −.
Understand the principles (not the names) of the commutative, associative and distributive laws as they apply to multiplication.

49–51
- **Find remainders after division**
Divide a whole number of pounds by 2, 4, 5 or 10 to give £.p.
Round up or down after division, depending on the context.

Rapid recall of multiplication and division facts

52
- **Know by heart:**
multiplication facts for 2, 3, 4, 5 and 10 times-tables.

56–59
- Begin to know:
multiplication facts for 6, 7, 8 and 9 times-tables.
- **Derive quickly:**
52
division facts corresponding to 2, 3, 4, 5 and 10 times-tables;
53
doubles of all whole numbers to 50 (e.g. 38 + 38, or 38 × 2);
doubles of multiples of 10 to 500 (e.g. 460 × 2);
doubles of multiples of 100 to 5000 (e.g. 3400 × 2);
and the corresponding halves (e.g. 74 ÷ 2, $\frac{1}{2}$ of 420, half of 3800).

Mental calculation strategies (× and ÷)

54–55
- Use doubling or halving, starting from known facts. For example: double/halve two-digit numbers by doubling/halving the tens first;
to multiply by 4, double, then double again;
to multiply by 5, multiply by 10 then halve;
to multiply by 20, multiply by 10 then double;
find the 8 times-table facts by doubling the 4 times-table;
find quarters by halving halves.

60
- Use closely related facts (e.g. to multiply by 9 or 11, multiply by 10 and adjust; develop the ×6 table from the ×4 and ×2 tables).

60
- Partition (e.g. 23 × 4 = (20 × 4) + (3 × 4)).
45, 47
- Use the relationship between multiplication and division.
61–63
- Use known number facts and place value to multiply and divide integers, including by 10 and then 100 (whole-number answers).

Pencil and paper procedures (× and ÷)

64–67
- Approximate first. Use informal pencil and paper methods to support, record or explain multiplications and division.
Develop and refine written methods for TU × U, TU ÷ U.

Checking results of calculations

41–42,
67
- Check with the inverse operation.

36
- Check the sum of several numbers by adding in reverse order.
65
- Check with an equivalent calculation.
66
- Estimate and check by approximating (round to nearest 10 or 100).

16
- Use knowledge of sums or differences of odd/even numbers.

Solving problems

Making decisions

68–71 • **Choose and use appropriate number operations and appropriate ways of calculating (mental, mental with jottings, pencil and paper) to solve problems.**
(For examples of problems see pages 78, 82–89, 100.)

Reasoning about numbers and shapes

11, 101 • Explain methods and reasoning about numbers orally and in writing.

11, 44 • Solve mathematical problems or puzzles, recognise and
124–125 explain patterns and relationships, generalise and predict. Suggest extensions by asking 'What if...?'

69, 93 • Make and investigate a general statement about familiar numbers or shapes by finding examples that satisfy it.

Problems involving 'real life', money and measures

70–73 • Use all four operations to solve word problems involving numbers in 'real life', money and measures (including time), using one or more steps, including converting pounds to pence and metres to centimetres and vice versa.

Handling data

Organising and interpreting data

110– • Solve a problem by collecting quickly, organising,
117 representing and interpreting data in tables, charts, graphs and diagrams, including those generated by a computer, for example: tally charts and frequency tables;
pictograms – symbol representing 2, 5, 10 or 20 units;
bar charts – intervals labelled in 2s, 5s, 10s or 20s;
Venn and Carroll diagrams (two criteria).

Measures, shape and space

Measures

74–81 • Use, read and write standard metric units (km, m, cm, mm, kg, g, l, ml), including their abbreviations, and imperial units (mile, pint).

74–81 • **Know and use the relationships between familiar units of length, mass and capacity.**
Know the equivalent of one half, one quarter, three quarters and one tenth of 1 km, 1 m, 1 kg, 1 litre in m, cm, g, ml. Convert up to 1000 centimetre to metres, and vice versa.

74–81 • Suggest suitable units and measuring equipment to estimate or measure length, mass or capacity.
Record estimates and readings from scales to a suitable degree of accuracy.

82–83 • Measure and calculate the perimeter and area of rectangles and other simple shapes, using counting methods and standard units (cm, cm^2).

84–90 • Use, read and write the vocabulary related to time.
Estimate/check times using seconds, minutes, hours.
Read the time from an analogue clock to the nearest minute, and from a 12-hour digital clock.
Use am and pm and the notation 9:53.
Read simple timetables and use this year's calendar.

Shape and space

92–93 • Describe and visualise 3-D and 2-D shapes, including the tetrahedron and heptagon.
Recognise equilateral and isosceles triangles.
Classify polygons using criteria such as number of right angles, whether or not they are regular, symmetry properties.

91 • Make shapes: for example, construct polygons by paper
96 folding or using pinboard, and discuss properties such as
97 lines of symmetry.
Visualise 3-D shapes from 2-D drawings and identify simple nets of solid shapes.

98–100 • Sketch the reflection of a simple shape in a mirror line parallel to one side (all sides parallel or perpendicular to the mirror line).

102– • Recognise positions and directions: for example, describe and
107 find the position of a point on a grid of squares where the lines are numbered.
Recognise simple examples of horizontal and vertical lines.
Use the eight compass directions N, S, E, W, NE, NW, SE, SW.

108–9 • Make and measure clockwise and anti-clockwise turns: for example, from SW to N, or from 4 to 10 on a clock face. Begin to know that angles are measured in degrees and that:
one whole turn is 360° or 4 right angles;
a quarter turn is 90° or one right angle;
half a right angle is 45°.
Start to order a set of angles less than 180°.

pages 2 and 3

A

1 211	5 478	9 515
2 196	6 298	10 209
3 304	7 628	
4 832	8 253	

11 one hundred and eighty-eight kilometres
12 two hundred and ninety-one kilometres
13 three hundred and twenty-five kilometres
14 four hundred and sixty kilometres
15 three hundred and thirty-three kilometres
16 eighty-seven kilometres
17 eight hundred and eighty-five kilometres
18 six hundred and thirty-nine kilometres
19 three hundred and sixty-four kilometres
20 seven hundred and twenty-one kilometres

B

1

River	Length (km)
Amazon	6750
Nile	6670
Yangtze	6300
Mississippi	6020
Yenisey	5540
Hwang He	5464
Ob	5409
Parana	4880
Congo	4700
Lena	4400

2 four thousand one hundred and ninety-four miles
3 four thousand one hundred and forty-five miles
4 three thousand nine hundred and fifteen miles
5 three thousand seven hundred and forty-one miles
6 three thousand four hundred and forty-two miles
7 three thousand three hundred and ninety-five miles
8 three thousand three hundred and sixty-one miles
9 three thousand and thirty-two miles
10 two thousand nine hundred and twenty miles
11 two thousand seven hundred and thirty-four miles

C

1 250 000   2 500 000   3 100 000   4 £750 000
5 a) 25 079   25 097   25 709   25 790   25 907
     25 970   27 059   27 095   27 509   27 590
     27 905   27 950
   b) twenty-five thousand and seventy-nine
      twenty-five thousand and ninety-seven
      twenty-five thousand seven hundred and nine
      twenty-five thousand seven hundred and ninety
      twenty-five thousand nine hundred and seven
      twenty-five thousand nine hundred and seventy
      twenty-seven thousand and fifty-nine
      twenty-seven thousand and ninety-five
      twenty-seven thousand five hundred and nine
      twenty-seven thousand five hundred and ninety
      twenty-seven thousand nine hundred and five
      twenty-seven thousand nine hundred and fifty

page 4

A

1 100 + 20 + 8		7 700 + 10 + 6
2 300 + 60 + 9		8 900 + 20 + 5
3 400 + 20 + 7		9 800 + 20 + 1
4 500 + 80 + 4		10 400 + 40 + 2
5 300 + 90 + 2		11 600 + 70 + 3
6 600 + 50 + 5		12 700 + 30 + 9
13 20		19 4
14 9		20 300
15 800		21 8
16 80		22 90
17 400		23 200
18 60		24 3

B

1 30	6 40	11 4000	16 30
2 500	7 7000	12 70	17 6
3 2000	8 2	13 300	18 700
4 5	9 9000	14 3000	
5 600	10 50	15 5	

19 1000 + 600 + 20 + 7
20 2000 + 400 + 50 + 2
21 3000 + 900 + 80 + 5
22 2000 + 100 + 70 + 4
23 4000 + 500 + 30 + 8
24 5000 + 800 + 40 + 3
25 7000 + 200 + 90 + 6
26 8000 + 300 + 10
27 2000 + 500 + 94   31 6000 + 523
28 1600 + 35   32 1200 + 77
29 300 + 89   33 4000 + 718
30 8000 + 194   34 2000 + 150 + 6

C

1 6137	11 614	21 −30
2 523	12 3436	22 −500
3 1208	13 5180	23 +6000
4 4710	14 542	24 −400
5 941	15 2275	25 +2000
6 2917	16 1879	26 +70
7 769	17 1415	27 +500
8 5634	18 636	28 −5000
9 627	19 6023	29 +80
10 608	20 3440	30 −600

page 5

A

1 40	9 50	17 2	25 59
2 70	10 910	18 3	26 40
3 90	11 600	19 5	27 77
4 80	12 730	20 10	28 84
5 160	13 20	21 70	29 30
6 200	14 500	22 14	30 56
7 380	15 670	23 24	31 100
8 520	16 1000	24 6	32 41
33 10	35 100	37 30	
34 50	36 120	38 200	

B

1	1760	7	4300	13	800	19	755
2	490	8	8350	14	216	20	409
3	5780	9	7010	15	57	21	936
4	3000	10	370	16	364	22	500
5	2240	11	1500	17	148	23	272
6	60	12	4670	18	320	24	640

25 63×10 29 565×10
26 $280 \div 10$ 30 $370 \div 10$
27 628×10 31 $8400 \div 10$
28 $2390 \div 10$ 32 21×10

C

1	3860	7	1400	13	300	19	500
2	632	8	17	14	1800	20	40 000
3	700	9	200	15	680	21	2300
4	6	10	1250	16	20 000	22	36 000
5	9470	11	4300	17	7000	23	9000
6	1000	12	25	18	14 300	24	100 000

25 100   27 1700
26 800   28 10 000

pages 6 and 7

A

1	570	7	924	13	292	19	814
2	835	8	299	14	440	20	897
3	805	9	416	15	575	21	381
4	420	10	823	16	389	22	178
5	207	11	530	17	983	23	24
6	557	12	929	18	866	24	317

25 250, 251, 252   29 381, 380, 379
26 698, 708, 718   30 407, 417, 427
27 511, 501, 491   31 406, 396, 386
28 479, 379, 279   32 635, 735, 835

B

1	332	9	2212	17	4271	25	548
2	547	10	2464	18	8952	26	289
3	801	11	4135	19	6503	27	175
4	1025	12	3590	20	10 487	28	431
5	352	13	483	21	1865	29	4310
6	268	14	80	22	2987	30	3687
7	631	15	892	23	740	31	3041
8	487	16	646	24	6691	32	5856
33	3491	37	752	41	3161	45	1678
34	7580	38	403	42	5594	46	4301
35	1374	39	349	43	4070	47	3814
36	8900	40	796	44	2708	48	453

C

1

+	100	10	1	1000
1697	1797	1707	1698	2697
399	499	409	400	1399
2914	3014	2924	2915	3914
4979	5079	4989	4980	5979

2

−	10	100	1000	1
3210	3200	3110	2210	3209
1398	1388	1298	398	1397
2107	2097	2007	1107	2106
4052	4042	3952	3052	4051

3	**395**	9	1347	15	6029	21	1103
4	1288	10	794	16	3182	22	1193
5	2411	11	1585	17	360	23	203
6	1069	12	5116	18	480	24	5319
7	1637	13	930	19	579	25	5310
8	3117	14	6701	20	1479	26	6309

27 3000   29 3099   31 3990
28 3009   30 3999   32 3900

pages 8 and 9

A

1	68	5	267	9	43	13	162
2	39	6	159	10	98	14	654
3	315	7	345	11	932	15	432
4	428	8	718	12	584	16	287

17 238, 283, 382, 823   19 325, 352, 523, 532
18 174, 417, 471, 714   20 469, 496, 649, 694
21 215   23 550   25 True   27 False
22 100   24 305   26 True   28 False

B

1 >   7 <
2 =   8 >
3 <   9 =
4 =   10 <
5 <   11 =
6 >   12 >

13 2536, 2635, 3256, 3526   19 1305
14 1498, 1849, 1948, 4189   20 575
15 6472, 6724, 7246, 7462   21 2050
16 3478, 3748, 3784, 3874   22 200
17 1456, 1465, 1546, 1654   23 1380
18 3187, 3781, 3817, 3871   24 1950

C

1 >   5 =   9 =
2 <   6 <   10 <
3 =   7 >   11 =
4 >   8 <   12 >

13 a) 1695   14 3560   18 1000
   b) 606   15 2250   19 2060
   c) 741   16 4570   20 1470
   d) 26   17 20 500   21 17 285

page 10

A

1 1, 3   3 2, 16   5 50, 85
2 3, 5   4 20, 30   6 10, 20

B

1 4, 14   3 5, 30   5 25, 45
2 2, 8   4 40, 60   6 300, 700
7 a) Wednesday   b) Monday   c) Tuesday

C

1 40, 90   3 5, 20   5 20, 40
2 20, 30   4 3, 15   6 30, 38

page 11

A

1 2, 3   3 4, 5   5 5, 5   7 5, 10
2 2, 7   4 2, 10   6 3, 6   8 4, 4

B

1 32	**2** 28	**3** 36	**4** 45	**5** 72	**6** 64

C

1 11, 12	**9** 24, 25	**17** 32, 33, 34
2 14, 15	**10** 26, 27	**18** 110, 111, 112
3 17, 18	**11** 30, 31	**19** 41, 42, 43
4 12, 13	**12** 28, 29	**20** 100, 101, 102
5 19, 20	**13** 4, 5, 6	**21** 86, 87, 88
6 15, 16	**14** 8, 9, 10	**22** 36, 37, 38
7 22, 23	**15** 14, 15, 16	**23** 149, 150, 151
8 20, 21	**16** 19, 20, 21	**24** 78, 79, 80

page 12

A

1 20	**4** 80	**7** 80	**10** 90	**13** 60	**16** 90
2 40	**5** 70	**8** 40	**11** 60	**14** 30	**17** 100
3 50	**6** 50	**9** 30	**12** 20	**15** 70	**18** 20

B

1 20	**4** 130	**7** 200	**10** 400
2 80	**5** 250	**8** 700	**11** 900
3 70	**6** 100	**9** 400	**12** 900
13 120	**15** 100	**17** 80	**19** 100
14 130	**16** 40	**18** 90	**20** 80

C

1 710	**6** 9200	**11** 9000	**16** 610
2 250	**7** 4300	**12** 9000	**17** 180
3 1490	**8** 1400	**13** 260	**18** 320
4 2640	**9** 5000	**14** 810	**19** 210
5 800	**10** 7000	**15** 200	**20** 450

21 about 3000	**23** about 135 000
22 about 1000	**24** about 30 000

page 13

A

1 7, 9, 11, 13, 15, 17
2 15, 20, 25, 30, 35, 40
3 4, 8, 12, 16, 20, 24
4 15, 18, 21, 24, 27, 30
5 33, 43, 53, 63, 73, 83
6 7, 14, 21, 28, 35, 42
7 34, 32, 30, 28, 26, 24
8 97, 87, 77, 67, 57, 47
9 22, 19, 16, 13, 10, 7
10 26, 21, 16, 11, 6, 1
11 36, 30, 24, 18, 12, 6
12 30, 26, 22, 18, 14, 10

B

1 . . . . 42, 48, 54
2 . . . . 45, 43, 41
3 . . . . 84, 87, 90
4 . . . . 80, 100, 120
5 54, 49, 44 . . . .
6 66, 62, 58 . . . .
7 24, 31, 38 . . . .
8 45, 42, 39 . . . .
9 4, 12, 20, 28, 36, 44
10 48, 42, 36, 30, 24, 18
11 25, 50, 75, 100, 125, 150
12 63, 54, 45, 36, 27, 18

C

1 65, 67, 69	Add 2
2 110, 106, 102	Subtract 4
3 74, 81, 88	Add 7
4 29, 20, 11	Subtract 9
5 190, 230, 270	Add 40
6 125, 122, 119	Subtract 3
7 135, 160, 185	Add 25
8 60, 68, 76	Add 8
9 58, 53, 48	Subtract 5
10 72, 87, 102	Add 15
11 375, 350, 325	Subtract 25
12 81, 87, 93	Add 6
13 45, 30, 15	Subtract 15
14 65, 58, 51	Subtract 7
15 39, 47, 55	Add 8
16 687, 798, 909	Add 111
17 31, 34, 37	Add 3
18 97, 86, 75	Subtract 11

pages 14 and 15

A

1 -6	**4** 0	**7** 2
2 -2	**5** 1	**8** 6
3 5	**6** 1	

9 $-5, -4, -3, -2, -1, 0, 1, 2, 3, 4, 5$
10 $-10, -8, -6, -4, -2, 0, 2, 4, 6, 8, 10$
11 $5, 4, 3, 2, 1, 0, -1, -2, -3, -4, -5$
12 $10, 8, 6, 4, 2, 0, -2, -4, -6, -8, -10$
13 $A = -1°C$ $B = -4°C$ $C = 3°C$
14 B
15 a) $3°C$ b) $7°C$ c) $4°C$
16 a) $-1°C$ b) $1°C$

B

1 1	**4** 2	**7** -7
2 -2	**5** -3	**8** -9
3 4	**6** -7	

9 $3, 2, 1, 0, -1, -2, -3$
10 $-2, -1, 0, 1, 2, 3, 4$
11 $0, -2, -4, -6, -8, -10, -12$
12 $-10, -9, -8, -7, -6, -5, -4$
13 $-10, -8, -6, -4, -2, 0, 2$
14 $-7, -5, -3, -1, 1, 3, 5$
15 $6, 4, 2, 0, -2, -4, -6$
16 $5, 3, 1, -1, -3, -5, -7$
17 $A = -1°C$ $B = -7°C$ $C = 6°C$
18 B
19 a) $6°C$ b) $7°C$ c) $13°C$
20 a) $-8°C$ b) $2°C$

C

1 2
2 4
3 8
4 4
5 6
6 6
7 4
8 5
9 $-3, -1, 0, 2, 5$
10 $-5, -3, -1, 1, 4$
11 $-4, -2, 0, 1, 3$
12 $-4, -1, 0, 2, 4$

13

Monday	Change	Tuesday
3°C	−4°C	−1°C
−1°C	+3°C	2°C
0°C	−5°C	−5°
4°C	−7°C	−3°C
−6°C	+2°C	−4°C
−2°C	+4°C	2°C

14

Monday	Change	Tuesday
7°C	−4°C	3°C
−2°C	+5°C	3°C
−4°C	+3°C	−1°C
1°C	−4°C	−3°C
0°C	−6°C	−6°C
−3°C	+7°C	4°C

page 16

A

1   3, 7, 31, 49, 65, 83   2   6, 18, 24, 52, 78, 94

B

1   103, 217, 729, 339, 951, 257, 865, 175, 583, 691, 207, 413

2   104, 218, 728, 340, 950, 256, 864, 176, 582, 692, 206, 412

C

1   4 odd, 2 even   5   odd
2   6 odd, 0 even   6   even
3   6 even, 0 odd   7   even
4   4 even, 2 odd   8   odd

page 17

A

1   2, 4, 6, 8, 10   4   3, 6, 9, 12, 15
2   5, 10, 15, 20, 25   5   4, 8, 12, 16, 20
3   10, 20, 30, 40, 50   6   6, 12, 18, 24, 30
7   True   11   False   15   False   19   True
8   True   12   True   16   True   20   False
9   False   13   True   17   True   21   False
10   False   14   True   18   False   22   True

B

1   41   7   15, 25, 30
2   34   8   18, 30
3   5   9   12 etc.
4   58   10   10 etc.
5   14, 18, 30   11   6 etc.
6   9, 15, 18, 27, 30   12   15 etc.

C

1   12, 20, 24, 36, 42, 60   5   20, 40, etc.
2   15, 20, 25, 60   6   21, 42, etc.
3   12, 18, 24, 36, 42, 60   7   36, 72, etc.
4   18, 36   8   30, 60, etc.
9   24, 26, 32, 34, 36, 42, 46, 52, 54, 56, 62, 64
10   25, 35, 45, 65
11   24, 32, 36, 52, 56, 64
12   24, 36, 42, 45, 54, 63
13   a) 48   c) 42   e) 54
     b) 66   d) 120   f) 90

pages 18 and 19

A

1 $\frac{1}{2}$ 3 $\frac{3}{5}$ 5 $\frac{2}{5}$ 7 $\frac{1}{3}$ 9 $\frac{1}{8}$ 11 $\frac{2}{3}$
2 $\frac{1}{6}$ 4 $\frac{1}{4}$ 6 $\frac{2}{6}$ 8 $\frac{5}{8}$ 10 $\frac{3}{4}$ 12 $\frac{1}{10}$

B

1 $\frac{1}{4}$ 5 $\frac{3}{4}$ 9 $\frac{3}{8}$
2 $\frac{5}{12}$ 6 $\frac{4}{6}$ 10 $\frac{3}{10}$
3 $\frac{2}{3}$ 7 $\frac{1}{6}$ 11 $\frac{1}{9}$
4 $\frac{5}{8}$ 8 $\frac{3}{5}$ 12 $\frac{6}{10}$

C

1 a) $\frac{5}{8}$ b) $\frac{3}{8}$ 7 a) $\frac{6}{20}$ b) $\frac{14}{20}$
2 a) $\frac{4}{9}$ b) $\frac{5}{9}$ 8 a) $\frac{7}{15}$ b) $\frac{8}{15}$
3 a) $\frac{3}{10}$ b) $\frac{7}{10}$ 9 a) $\frac{7}{12}$ b) $\frac{5}{12}$
4 a) $\frac{7}{16}$ b) $\frac{9}{16}$ 10 a) $\frac{1}{6}$ b) $\frac{5}{6}$
5 a) $\frac{1}{4}$ b) $\frac{3}{4}$ 11 a) $\frac{4}{12}$ b) $\frac{8}{12}$
6 a) $\frac{3}{8}$ b) $\frac{5}{8}$ 12 a) $\frac{9}{16}$ b) $\frac{7}{16}$

pages 20 and 21

A

1 $\frac{1}{4}=\frac{2}{8}$ 5 $\frac{1}{2}=\frac{3}{6}$ 9 $\frac{2}{5}=\frac{4}{10}$ 13 $\frac{3}{4}=\frac{12}{16}$
2 $\frac{1}{2}=\frac{2}{4}$ 6 $\frac{2}{3}=\frac{4}{6}$ 10 $\frac{4}{5}=\frac{8}{10}$ 14 $\frac{3}{5}=\frac{6}{10}$
3 $\frac{3}{4}=\frac{6}{8}$ 7 $\frac{1}{5}=\frac{2}{10}$ 11 $\frac{1}{4}=\frac{2}{8}$ 15 $\frac{2}{3}=\frac{6}{9}$
4 $\frac{1}{3}=\frac{2}{6}$ 8 $\frac{1}{2}=\frac{5}{10}$ 12 $\frac{1}{3}=\frac{4}{12}$ 16 $\frac{1}{2}=\frac{6}{12}$

B

1 $1=\frac{3}{3}$ 4 $\frac{1}{2}=\frac{3}{6}$ 7 $\frac{1}{2}=\frac{4}{8}$ 10 $\frac{1}{2}=\frac{5}{10}$
2 $\frac{1}{2}=\frac{2}{4}$ 5 $\frac{1}{5}=\frac{2}{10}$ 8 $1=\frac{10}{10}$ 11 $1=\frac{8}{8}$
3 $\frac{2}{5}=\frac{4}{10}$ 6 $1=\frac{6}{6}$ 9 $\frac{1}{4}=\frac{2}{8}$ 12 $\frac{1}{3}=\frac{2}{6}$
13 $\frac{1}{2}=\frac{2}{4}=\frac{3}{6}=\frac{4}{8}=\frac{5}{10}=\frac{6}{12}=\frac{7}{14}=\frac{8}{16}=\frac{9}{18}=\frac{10}{20}$
14 $\frac{1}{3}=\frac{2}{6}=\frac{3}{9}=\frac{4}{12}=\frac{5}{15}=\frac{6}{18}=\frac{7}{21}=\frac{8}{24}=\frac{9}{27}=\frac{10}{30}$
15 $\frac{3}{4}=\frac{6}{8}=\frac{9}{12}=\frac{12}{16}=\frac{15}{20}=\frac{18}{24}=\frac{21}{28}=\frac{24}{32}=\frac{27}{36}=\frac{30}{40}$

C

1   >   5   =   9   >
2   =   6   >   10   =
3   <   7   =   11   <
4   >   8   <   12   >
13 $\frac{4}{12}$ 17 A $\frac{2}{20}$ E $\frac{3}{5}$
14 $\frac{10}{30}$ B $\frac{1}{4}$ F $\frac{3}{4}$
15 $\frac{8}{12}$ C $\frac{20}{50}$ G $\frac{8}{10}$
16 $\frac{20}{50}$ D $\frac{1}{2}$ H $\frac{95}{100}$

page 22

A

1   6   12   4   23   3p
2   12   13   9p   24   6p
3   9p   14   5p   25   5 cm
4   20p   15   8 cm   26   10
5   50 cm   16   2   27   8
6   8   17   1   28   7p
7   15   18   7p   29   2p
8   30p   19   10p   30   9 cm
9   14p   20   6 cm   31   17
10   25 cm   21   4
11   3   22   20

B

1 11	**3** 8	**5** 5 cm	**7** 20p	**9** 20p
2 5	**4** 6	**6** 50 cm	**8** 10p	**10** 8p
11 $\frac{1}{10}$	**13** $\frac{1}{5}$	**15** $\frac{1}{100}$	**17** $\frac{1}{10}$	**19** a) 20
12 $\frac{1}{2}$	**14** $\frac{1}{4}$	**16** $\frac{1}{4}$	**18** $\frac{1}{2}$	b) 15

C

1 21	**3** 12	**5** 150	**7** 90 cm	**9** 30p
2 24	**4** 14	**6** 7	**8** 32 cm	**10** 51p
11 $\frac{1}{4}$	**13** $\frac{1}{10}$	**15** $\frac{1}{4}$	**17** $\frac{1}{8}$	**19** 8
12 $\frac{1}{20}$	**14** $\frac{1}{50}$	**16** $\frac{1}{20}$	**18** $\frac{1}{40}$	**20** 4

page 23

A

1

Number of tickets	Number of prizes
5	1
10	2
15	3
20	4
25	5
30	6
35	7
40	8
45	9
50	10

2

Number of tickets	Number of prizes
4	1
8	2
12	3
16	4
20	5
24	6
28	7
32	8
36	9
40	10

B

1 a) 1 in every 7   **3** a) 1 in every 2
   b) 6 to every 1   b) 1 to every 1
2 a) 1 in every 9
   b) 8 to every 1

C

1 12	**3** 50	**5** 10
2 32	**4** 31	**6** 49

pages 24 and 25

A

1 $\frac{3}{10}$ 0·3	**4** $\frac{7}{10}$ 0·7	**7** $\frac{10}{10}$ 1·0
2 $\frac{9}{10}$ 0·9	**5** $\frac{2}{10}$ 0·2	**8** $\frac{4}{10}$ 0·4
3 $\frac{1}{2}$ or $\frac{5}{10}$ 0·5	**6** $\frac{1}{10}$ 0·1	**9** $\frac{6}{10}$ 0·6

10 $\frac{8}{10}$ 0·8   **12** a) $\frac{1}{2}$ or $\frac{5}{10}$ b) 0·5
11 a) $\frac{2}{10}$ b) 0·2   **13** a) $\frac{9}{10}$ b) 0·9

B

1 0·2	**7** $\frac{8}{10}$	**13** 3
2 0·5	**8** 4	**14** $\frac{6}{10}$
3 0·9	**9** $\frac{7}{10}$	**15** 9
4 1·1	**10** 5	**16** $\frac{4}{10}$
5 1·3	**11** 10	**17** $\frac{5}{10}$
6 1·7	**12** $\frac{1}{10}$	**18** 6

19 0·6, 0·7, 0·8, 0·9, 1·0   **21** 3·0, 3·5, 4·0, 4·5, 5·0
20 1·2, 1·4, 1·6, 1·8, 2·0   **22** 1·1, 1·3, 1·5, 1·7, 1·9

23 0·7	**27** 0·3	**31** 1·9
24 0·5	**28** 0·6	**32** 1·4
25 0·8	**29** 1·8	**33** 1·2
26 0·4	**30** 1·7	**34** 1·4

35 0·5 − 0·2	**41** 1·3 + 0·6
36 0·4 + 0·5	**42** 1·8 − 0·2
37 0·8 − 0·4	**43** 1·1 + 0·7
38 0·6 + 0·1	**44** 1·5 − 0·3
39 0·9 − 0·3	**45** 1·2 + 0·4
40 0·2 + 0·5	**46** 1·9 − 0·2

C

1 3·17	**11** $\frac{9}{10}$	**21** 5	**31** 1·8
2 1·82	**12** 6	**22** 8	**32** 0·8
3 4·35	**13** $\frac{9}{10}$	**23** $\frac{3}{100}$	**33** 1·0
4 3·6	**14** 30	**24** $\frac{5}{10}$	**34** 1·7
5 0·41	**15** $\frac{7}{10}$	**25** 1·9	**35** 0·4
6 2·03	**16** 7	**26** 3·0	**36** 1·3
7 $\frac{9}{10}$	**17** $\frac{3}{10}$	**27** 1·0	**37** 3·4
8 10	**18** $\frac{7}{100}$	**28** 0·9	**38** 3·2
9 4	**19** $\frac{2}{10}$	**29** 4·3	**39** 2·4
10 $\frac{7}{10}$	**20** $\frac{4}{100}$	**30** 3·4	**40** 3·9

page 26

A

1 16	**3** 8·0	**5** 1·9	**7** 3·2	**9** 4
2 2·0	**4** 5	**6** 8	**8** 6·7	**10** 6·3

11   0·2   0·4   0·5   0·7   0·9

B

1 <	**3** =	**5** >	**7** =
2 >	**4** <	**6** <	**8** >

9 3·6, 4·7, 6·3, 7·4   **12** 3, 3·5, 5, 5·3
10 2·2, 2·9, 9·2, 9·9   **13** 4·8, 8, 8·4, 48
11 1·2, 2·1, 12, 21   **14** 7, 7·7, 7·9, 9·7

C

1 3·4, 4·3, 33·4, 43, 43·3
2 1·9, 9·01, 9·1, 11·9, 19·1
3 1·4, 1·41, 4·1, 11·4, 14·1
4 7·73, 7·83, 8·37, 8·7, 8·73
5 5·69, 5·96, 9·5, 9·6, 9·65
6   0·91   0·94   0·97   1·0   1·05   1·08
   0·9 ↓   ↓   ↓   ↓   ↓   ↓ 1·1

page 27

A

1   0·1
2   0·25
3   0·5
4   0·3

5   0·75
6   0·6
7   £0·20
8   77p

9   41p
10   £0·13
11   99p
12   50p

13   $\frac{1}{2} = 0·5$ $\frac{3}{4} = 0·75$
        $\frac{1}{10} = 0·1$ $\frac{1}{4} = 0·25$
        $\frac{7}{10} = 0·7$ $\frac{4}{10} = 0·4$

B

1   $\frac{4}{10}$
2   $\frac{1}{2}$
3   $\frac{1}{10}$
4   $\frac{6}{10}$
5   $\frac{1}{4}$
6   $\frac{3}{10}$

7   £0·70
8   £0·10
9   £0·75
10   0·5 cm
11   0·8 m
12   0·2 m

13   >
14   <
15   >
16   =

17

Decimals	Fractions
0·3	$\frac{3}{10}$
0·9	$\frac{9}{10}$
0·5	$\frac{1}{2}$
1·0	$\frac{10}{10}$
0·25	$\frac{1}{4}$
0·2	$\frac{2}{10}$
0·7	$\frac{7}{10}$
0·75	$\frac{3}{4}$
0·1	$\frac{1}{10}$

C

1   $1\frac{1}{2}$
2   $3\frac{8}{10}$
3   $7\frac{3}{10}$
4   $2\frac{7}{10}$
5   $4\frac{9}{10}$
6   $11\frac{6}{10}$
7   $5\frac{1}{4}$
8   $17\frac{43}{100}$

9   $6\frac{82}{100}$
10   $8\frac{3}{4}$
11   $13\frac{14}{100}$
12   $20\frac{9}{100}$
13   1·5
14   3·7
15   4·25
16   9·4

17   2·8
18   2·75
19   £6·90
20   £3·50
21   £0·72
22   1·75 m
23   5·3 cm
24   0·73 m

25   0·12, 0·2, $\frac{1}{2}$ 27 $\frac{7}{100}$, 0·17, 0·7
26   $\frac{3}{10}$, 0·34, $\frac{3}{4}$ 28 $\frac{1}{4}$, $\frac{4}{10}$, 0·44
29   0·55   31   0·53   33   0·62
30   0·3   32   0·77   34   0·39

pages 28 and 29

A

1   100
2   52
3   103
4   104
5   59
6   47
7   1000

8   28
9   584
10   79
11   1400
12   87
13   True
14   True

15   False
16   True
17   False
18   True
19   False
20   False
21   True

22   272, 472, 358, 542

B

1   184
2   53
3   66
4   167
5   38

6   125
7   171
8   27
9   700
10   172

11   37
12   38
13   67
14   75
15   63

16   49
17   58
18   58

19   700 + 400
20   47 + 20
21   38 + 31
22   474 + 26

23   26 + 38
24   320 + 36
25   63 + 37
26   66 + 19

C

1   107
2   142
3   197

4   98
5   127
6   138

7   139
8   117
9   156

10   135
11   157
12   147

13   800 + 900
14   500 + 741
15   6·3 + 0·7
16   230 + 280
17   75 + 61

18   640 + 180
19   359 + 430
20   412 + 120
21   169 + 49
22   0·4 + 0·6

24   328   2813
      498   2815
      774   2983
      776   2985
    2537   3261

pages 30 and 31

A

1   65
2   8
3   26
4   291
5   52
6   600
7   120 − 30
8   238 − 7
9   273 − 9
10   59 − 35
11   134 − 40
12   814 − 100
13   68 − 41
14   704 − 10
15   500 − 8

16   1200 − 500
17   96 − 29
18   135 − 11
19   124
20   67
21   242
22   337
23   114
24   82
25   25
26   3
27   85
28   700
29   **500**
30   800

B

1   262
2   32
7   74 − 38
8   503 − 495
9   1200 − 400
10   64 − 29
11   600 − 542
12   135 − 48

3   56
4   64

5   108
6   72

13   1000 − 850
14   276 − 21
15   3000 − 2996
16   100 − 53
17   130 − 60
18   217 − 50

19   133
20   226
21   52
22   317
23   179
24   126

25   62
26   26
27   59
28   650
29   950
30   450

31   42
32   57
33   25
34   111
35   69
36   53

C

1   165
2   2005
3   340

4   446
5   772
6   314

7   209
8   262

10

Name	Paper A	Paper B	Total
Total	80	80	160
Emily	77	75	152
Oliver	74	72	146
Nathan	71	69	140
Kerry	68	57	125
Tracey	62	59	121
Anil	58	59	117
Ben	63	50	113
Rachel	65	46	111
Craig	59	45	104
Jeremy	49	39	88
Charlene	46	37	83

11 25   107   112   132   137   244

12 161 miles

page 32

A

1 14	**6** 13	**11** 16
2 14	**7** 15	**12** 17
3 13	**8** 18	**13** 13
4 16	**9** 14	**14** 16
5 17	**10** 15	**15** 15

16 $85 + 15$
$15 + 85$
$45 + 55$
$35 + 65$
$95 + 5$
$75 + 25$

17 $400 + 600$
$900 + 100$
$800 + 200$
$700 + 300$
$500 + 500$
$300 + 700$

B

1 140	**6** 150	**11** 140
2 160	**7** 1400	**12** 160
3 160	**8** 1800	**13** 1300
4 140	**9** 1700	**14** 1300
5 150	**10** 1500	**15** 1600

16 $47 + 53$
$14 + 86$
$39 + 61$
$91 + 9$
$55 + 45$
$73 + 27$

17 $350 + 650$
$450 + 550$
$150 + 850$
$250 + 750$
$650 + 350$
$50 + 950$

C

1 $60 + 110$	**6** $700 + 600$
2 $50 + 90$	**7** $0.9 + 0.9$
3 $70 + 70$	**8** $0.8 + 0.7$
4 $600 + 800$	**9** $0.8 + 0.8$
5 $700 + 900$	**10** $0.8 + 0.9$

11 a) $490 + 510$
$140 + 860$
$730 + 270$
$260 + 740$
$520 + 480$
$810 + 190$

b) $0.3 + 0.7$
$0.9 + 0.1$
$0.5 + 0.5$
$0.2 + 0.8$
$0.7 + 0.3$
$0.1 + 0.9$

page 33

A

1 8	**6** 7	**11** 8
2 9	**7** 9	**12** 7
3 8	**8** 8	**13** 7
4 6	**9** 8	**14** 6
5 7	**10** 9	**15** 9

16 $95 = 5$
$25 = 75$
$65 = 35$
$55 = 45$
$75 = 25$
$5 = 95$

17 $700 = 300$
$600 = 400$
$100 = 900$
$200 = 800$
$400 = 600$
$900 = 100$

B

1 70	**6** 90	**11** 60
2 70	**7** 800	**12** 700
3 90	**8** 800	**13** 800
4 90	**9** 700	**14** 90
5 90	**10** 800	**15** 600

16 $52 = 48$
$23 = 77$
$46 = 54$
$81 = 19$
$18 = 82$
$67 = 33$

17 $550 = 450$
$150 = 850$
$250 = 750$
$50 = 950$
$450 = 550$
$850 = 150$

C

1 $160 - 80$	**6** $1400 - 700$
2 $150 - 80$	**7** $1.5 - 0.7$
3 $170 - 80$	**8** $1.6 - 0.7$
4 $1500 - 900$	**9** $1.7 - 0.9$
5 $1800 - 900$	**10** $0.8 + 0.9$

11 a) $690 = 310$
$470 = 530$
$710 = 290$
$560 = 440$
$140 = 860$
$320 = 680$

b) $0.4 = 0.6$
$0.6 = 0.4$
$0.1 = 0.9$
$0.5 = 0.5$
$0.8 = 0.2$
$0.2 = 0.8$

12 $140 - 20$
$1500 - 700$
$156 - 76$
$1.0 - 0.3$

page 34 (counting up)

A

1 6	**3** 9	**5** 18	**7** 14	**9** 19
2 4	**4** 7	**6** 23	**8** 8	**10** 13

B

1 5	**3** 8	**5** 107	**7** 17	**9** 32
2 112	**4** 8	**6** 210	**8** 58	**10** 19

C

1 $604 - 418$	**6** $6018 - 2025$
2 $703 - 429$	**7** $9012 - 4014$
3 $6000 - 2125$	**8** $9000 - 3307$
4 $512 - 315$	**9** $7000 - 3124$
5 $915 - 417$	**10** $3008 - 1023$

page 34 (partitioning)

A

1 78	**3** 33	**5** 88	**7** 53	**9** 89
2 67	**4** 44	**6** 79	**8** 64	**10** 45

B

1 83	**3** 44	**5** 95	**7** 42	**9** 84
2 83	**4** 28	**6** 95	**8** 38	**10** 29

C

1 $326 + 252$	**6** $857 - 505$
2 $438 + 246$	**7** $649 - 583$
3 $428 + 108$	**8** $736 - 222$
4 $174 - 148$	**9** $462 - 321$
5 $283 - 219$	**10** $525 - 307$

page 35 (near doubles)

A

1 33	**3** 36	**5** 430	**7** 310	**9** 550
2 51	**4** 34	**6** 270	**8** 830	**10** 290

B

1 68	**3** 94	**5** 720	**7** 560	**9** 920
2 57	**4** 85	**6** 350	**8** 770	**10** 540

C

1 51 + 53	**6** 780 + 760
2 72 + 71	**7** 870 + 880
3 530 + 540	**8** 590 + 590
4 680 + 680	**9** 660 + 650
5 89 + 88	**10** 950 + 940

page 35 (+/− and adjust)

A

1 71	**5** 73	**9** 67
2 29	**6** 46	**10** 37
3 57	**7** 94	
4 38	**8** 63	

B

1 102	**5** 79	**9** 107
2 48	**6** 42	**10** 105
3 145	**7** 136	
4 56	**8** 115	

C

1 256 + 68	**6** 486 + 61
2 232 − 39	**7** 191 + 72
3 765 + 52	**8** 315 − 48
4 179 + 59	**9** 418 + 96
5 468 − 99	**10** 69 + 78

page 36 (+/− relationship)

A

1 23 + 16 = 39	**2** 46 + 17 = 63
16 + 23 = 39	17 + 46 = 63
39 − 16 = 23	63 − 17 = 46
39 − 23 = 16	63 − 46 = 17

B

1 48 + 16 = 64	**6** 86 − 17 = 69
16 + 48 = 64	86 − 69 = 17
64 − 48 = 16	69 + 17 = 86
64 − 16 = 48	17 + 69 = 86
2 67 − 29 = 38	**7** 44 + 27 = 71
67 − 38 = 29	27 + 44 = 71
38 + 29 = 67	71 − 44 = 27
29 + 38 = 67	71 − 27 = 44
3 45 + 38 = 83	**8** 95 − 39 = 56
38 + 45 = 83	95 − 56 = 39
83 − 45 = 38	56 + 39 = 95
83 − 38 = 45	39 + 56 = 95
4 58 − 26 = 32	**9** 53 + 28 = 81
58 − 32 = 26	28 + 53 = 81
32 + 26 = 58	81 − 53 = 28
26 + 32 = 58	81 − 28 = 53
5 37 + 57 = 94	**10** 74 − 46 = 28
57 + 37 = 94	74 − 28 = 46
94 − 57 = 37	46 + 28 = 74
94 − 37 = 57	28 + 46 = 74

C

1 123 + 214 = 337	**6** 153 + 62 = 215
214 + 123 = 337	62 + 153 = 215
337 − 214 = 123	215 − 153 = 62
337 − 123 = 214	215 − 62 = 153
2 72 + 37 = 109	**7** 510 + 290 = 800
37 + 72 = 109	290 + 510 = 800
109 − 72 = 37	800 − 510 = 290
109 − 37 = 72	800 − 290 = 510
3 430 + 170 = 600	**8** 480 + 420 = 900
170 + 430 = 600	420 + 480 = 900
600 − 430 = 170	900 − 480 = 420
600 − 170 = 430	900 − 420 = 480
4 360 + 340 = 700	**9** 327 + 164 = 491
340 + 360 = 700	164 + 327 = 491
700 − 360 = 340	491 − 327 = 164
700 − 340 = 360	491 − 164 = 327
5 146 + 73 = 219	**10** 568 + 119 = 687
73 + 146 = 219	119 + 568 = 687
219 − 146 = 73	687 − 568 = 119
219 − 73 = 146	687 − 119 = 568

page 36 (adding several numbers)

A

1 90	**3** 16	**5** 150	**7** 190	**9** 18
2 140	**4** 300	**6** 18	**8** 60	**10** 120

B

1 20	**3** 32	**5** 160	**7** 31	**9** 40
2 21	**4** 100	**6** 24	**8** 23	**10** 180

C

1 2 + 5 + 6 + 8 + 7
2 9 + 10 + 98 + 20
3 14 + 9 + 13
4 40 + 80 + 60 + 70
5 1 + 4 + 7 + 9 + 6
6 8 + 7 + 12 + 2
7 5 + 7 + 1 + 8 + 3
8 70 + 90 + 40 + 30
9 7 + 6 + 7 + 8
10 17 + 25 + 9 + 15

page 37

A

1

+	8	9	6
9	17	18	15
7	15	16	13
8	16	17	14

4

−	43	26	55
78	35	52	23
67	24	41	12
99	56	73	44

2

−	8	7	9
19	11	12	10
16	8	9	7
18	10	11	9

5

+	9	21	29
62	71	83	91
35	44	56	64
57	66	78	86

3

+	24	32	53
15	39	47	68
43	67	75	96
34	58	66	87

6

−	11	19	21
48	37	29	27
24	13	5	3
76	65	57	55

7

+	34	75	93
200	234	275	293
800	834	875	893
500	534	575	593

8

−	7	9	6
104	97	95	98
503	496	494	497
605	598	596	599

B

1 1273	5 1300	9 45	13 120
2 90	6 471	10 557	14 93
3 293	7 117	11 71	15 396
4 68	8 7994	12 47	16 8
17 99	22 287	27 45	
18 72	23 24	28 19	
19 96	24 72	29 43 + 57	
20 105	25 47	30 92+8	
21 357	26 27	31 14 + 86	

c

1 450 + 280	9 5002 − 103
2 720 − 290	10 567 + 33
3 4005 − 1012	11 740 − 460
4 8·3 − 6·5	12 4·2 + 0·8
5 360 + 190	13 350 + 160
6 985 − 565	14 1231 − 531
7 1361 − 800	15 329 + 71
8 6·2 + 3·8	

page 38

A

1 92	4 226	7 153	10 383
2 94	5 284	8 192	11 358
3 117	6 110	9 193	

B

1 272	4 593	7 243	10 394
2 385	5 784	8 511	11 249
3 628	6 436	9 689	12 383

c

1 821	6 1434	11 1201	
2 1215	7 1480	12 1661	
3 1094	8 1471	13 1051	
4 1204	9 1243	14 1264	
5 1233	10 1281	15 664	

page 39

A

1 92	3 91	5 119	7 183	9 172
2 95	4 118	6 184	8 195	10 117

B

1 235	5 385	9 638	13 609
2 385	6 271	10 592	
3 318	7 449	11 935	
4 536	8 196	12 533	

c

1 755	6 635	11 912
2 551	7 421	12 2301
3 453	8 944	13 £553
4 2457	9 2334	14 421
5 2737	10 2368	15 405

page 40

A

1 164	5 627	9 £5·61	13 £4·17
2 319	6 497	10 £7·10	
3 408	7 £4·18	11 £9·03	
4 328	8 £2·57	12 £6·33	

B

1 237	4 437	7 £4·90	10 £4·77
2 607	5 £1·91	8 £6·74	11 217
3 462	6 £2·85	9 £4·91	

C

1 2290	4 4134	7 £6·89	10 £9·12
2 4936	5 £2·88	8 £6·77	11 3247
3 1962	6 £4·24	9 £9·23	12 £15·07

page 41

A

1 23	4 38	7 27	10 39
2 28	5 26	8 28	11 56 years
3 36	6 19	9 47	

B

1 72	4 386	7 751	10 525
2 285	5 713	8 729	11 87
3 475	6 403	9 283	12 74

C

1 86	5 140	9 176	13 124
2 176	6 314	10 465	
3 485	7 189	11 155	
4 345	8 285	12 257	

page 42

A

1 36	5 23	9 36	
2 24	6 15	10 27	
3 18	7 28	11 28	
4 29	8 25	12 35	

B

1 125	4 358	7 67	10 378
2 145	5 276	8 209	11 £136
3 265	6 271	9 566	12 145 miles

C

1 94	5 376	9 167	13 487
2 313	6 315	10 446	14 667
3 118	7 54	11 153	
4 164	8 436	12 331	

page 43

A

1 105	4 181	7 £2·21	10 £1·27
2 116	5 135	8 £1·33	11 73
3 82	6 £1·12	9 £1·05	

B

1 83	5 382	9 £3·46	13 £5·89
2 179	6 283	10 £1·66	14 176
3 282	7 £1·34	11 £2·84	
4 49	8 £2·04	12 £1·75	

C

1 1183	**5** 5586	**9** £1·68	**13** £773
2 2253	**6** 6057	**10** £2·96	**14** £3·68
3 4564	**7** £1·56	**11** £0·92	
4 3037	**8** £2·86	**12** £4·58	

page 44

A

1

5	4	9
10	6	2
3	8	7

3

2	7	6
9	5	1
4	3	8

2

10	3	8
5	7	9
6	11	4

4

9	10	5
4	8	12
11	6	7

B

1

8	7	12
13	9	5
6	11	10

3

9	16	11
14	12	10
13	8	15

2

12	2	16
14	10	6
4	18	8

4

12	13	8
7	11	15
14	9	10

C

1

2	11	7	14
13	8	12	1
16	5	9	4
3	10	6	15

3

3	14	10	15
16	9	13	4
17	8	12	5
6	11	7	18

2

5	16	15	2
10	7	8	13
6	11	12	9
17	4	3	14

page 45

A

1

×2
4 → 8
5 → 10
9 → 18
7 → 14
8 → 16

3

×4
4 → 16
8 → 32
6 → 24
11 → 44
7 → 28

2

×3
4 → 12
10 → 30
7 → 21
9 → 27
6 → 18

4

×5
4 → 20
9 → 45
5 → 25
8 → 40
7 → 35

B

1 7 × 3	**5** 5 × 1	**9** 6 × 6
2 9 × 4	**6** 7 × 5	**10** 3 × 8
3 4 × 7	**7** 6 × 9	**11** 8 × 0
4 5 × 4	**8** 7 × 6	**12** 9 × 10

13 6 × 8 = 48   **16** 7 × 9 = 63
8 × 6 = 48   9 × 7 = 63
48 ÷ 8 = 6   63 ÷ 7 = 9
48 ÷ 6 = 8   63 ÷ 9 = 7

14 7 × 8 = 56   **17** 10 × 12 = 120
8 × 7 = 56   12 × 10 = 120
56 ÷ 7 = 8   120 ÷ 10 = 12
56 ÷ 8 = 7   120 ÷ 12 = 10

15 8 × 9 = 72   **18** 6 × 9 = 54
9 × 8 = 72   9 × 6 = 54
72 ÷ 8 = 9   54 ÷ 6 = 9
72 ÷ 9 = 8   54 ÷ 9 = 6

C

1 12 × 4	**5** 7 × 8	**9** 8 × 6
2 1 × 7	**6** 4 × 9	**10** 12 × 5
3 3 × 25	**7** 7 × 7	**11** 8 × 11
4 9 × 8	**8** 9 × 0	**12** 4 × 15

13

×	8	9	7
6	48	54	42
4	32	36	28
3	24	27	21

14

×	6	7	5
3	18	21	15
8	48	56	40
9	54	63	45

15

×	5	6	2
9	45	54	18
8	40	48	16
7	35	42	14

page 46

A

1 16	**5** 45	**9** 32
2 120	**6** 20	**10** 42
3 60	**7** 70	**11** 35
4 30	**8** 200	**12** 40

B

1 21	**5** 24	**9** 40
2 36	**6** 60	**10** 80 kg
3 200	**7** 120	
4 42	**8** 840	

C

1 27	**3** 720	**5** 504
2 56	**4** 84	**6** 168

7 12, 21, 24, 27, 28, 32, 36, 56, 63, 72

8 a) 13, 14   d) 34, 35
b) 25, 26   e) 32, 33
c) 28, 29   f) 37, 38

Answers

page 47

A

1
÷2
10 → 5
16 → 8
6 → 3
18 → 9
14 → 7

3
÷4
32 → 8
20 → 5
28 → 7
16 → 4
36 → 9

2
÷3
12 → 4
21 → 7
15 → 5
24 → 8
18 → 6

4
÷5
35 → 7
45 → 9
30 → 6
40 → 8
15 → 3

B

1 35 ÷ 7
2 8 ÷ 1
3 54 ÷ 9
4 56 ÷ 8
5 24 ÷ 2
6 36 ÷ 9
7 27 ÷ 3
8 130 ÷ 10
9 42 ÷ 6
10 24 ÷ 8
11 81 ÷ 9
12 6 ÷ 1
13 28 ÷ 7
14 48 ÷ 8
15 30 ÷ 6
16 63 ÷ 9

17 12 ÷ 6 = 2
12 ÷ 2 = 6
6 × 2 = 12
2 × 6 = 12
18 3 × 8 = 24
8 × 3 = 24
24 ÷ 3 = 8
24 ÷ 8 = 3

19 36 ÷ 4 = 9
36 ÷ 9 = 4
9 × 4 = 36
4 × 9 = 36
20 7 × 5 = 35
5 × 7 = 35
35 ÷ 5 = 7
35 ÷ 7 = 5

C

1
Input		Output
56	÷7	8
35	÷5	7
5	÷1	5
90	÷15	6
72	÷9	8
72	÷10	7·2

2
Input		Output
11	÷1	11
175	÷25	5
140	÷7	20
5	÷10	0·5
63	÷7	9
99	÷11	9

3
Input		Output
42	÷7	6
100	÷5	20
54	÷9	6
200	÷25	8
18	÷1	18
120	÷10	12

4 42

page 48

A

1 8   **3** 9   **5** 6   **7** 7   **9** 9
2 8   **4** 5   **6** 5   **8** 24   **10** £15

B

1 6   **3** 15   **5** 80 g
2 £5·00   **4** 9   **6** 15

C

1 150 ml   **3** 15   **5** 12 miles
2 5   **4** 37

page 49

A

1 10 × 2 + 1   **7** 9 × 3 + 1   **13** 8 r 5
2 7 × 5 + 2   **8** 5 × 4 + 3   **14** 6 r 3
3 7 × 10 + 3   **9** 18 × 2 + 1   **15** 7 r 1
4 21 × 2 + 1   **10** 4 r 1   **16** 8 r 2
5 4 × 5 + 4   **11** 3 r 1   **17** 6 r 3
6 3 × 10 + 1   **12** 11 r 1   **18** 8 r 2
19 7, 6 left over   **20** 6, 2 left over

B

1 10 r 1   **8** 5 r 3   **15** £6·60
2 5 r 2   **9** 7 r 2   **16** £17·50
3 9 r 1   **10** 4 r 1   **17** £5·25
4 11 r 3   **11** £11·50   **18** £6·30
5 13 r 4   **12** £5·20   **19** £8·40
6 18 r 1   **13** £6·50   **20** £9·75
7 9 r 1   **14** £8·50
21 8, 2 left over
22 £7·50

C

1 15 r 3   **7** 14 r 2   **13** £63·10   **19** £1·70
2 7 r 2   **8** 11 r 3   **14** £13·75   **20** £1·75
3 7 r 4   **9** 6 r 5   **15** £18·40   **21** £3·75
4 7 r 2   **10** 2 r 26   **16** £3·65   **22** £4·50
5 4 r 21   **11** £15·20   **17** £1·20   **23** £3·80
6 12 r 8   **12** £28·50   **18** £1·85

pages 50 and 51

A

1 13   **3** 8   **5** 8   **7** 6   **9** 7
2 6   **4** 7   **6** 13   **8** 9   **10** 8

B

1 11   **3** 11   **5** 8   **7** 17   **9** 5
2 7   **4** 13   **6** 10   **8** 7   **10** 6

C

1 15   **3** 8   **5** 5   **7** 13   **9** 5
2 8   **4** 5   **6** 16   **8** 9   **10** 9

page 52

A

1 16   **7** 21   **13** 24   **19** 40   **25** 40
2 8   **8** 30   **14** 36   **20** 25   **26** 90
3 14   **9** 24   **15** 12   **21** 35   **27** 60
4 12   **10** 15   **16** 40   **22** 45   **28** 100
5 18   **11** 27   **17** 28   **23** 30   **29** 80
6 10   **12** 18   **18** 16   **24** 15   **30** 70

B

1 9×2	9 7×4	17 $28 \div 4$
2 8×10	10 10×3	18 $24 \div 3$
3 6×3	11 7×10	19 $100 \div 10$
4 4×4	12 8×4	20 $40 \div 5$
5 5×3	13 $30 \div 10$	21 $30 \div 5$
6 9×5	14 $16 \div 2$	22 $36 \div 4$
7 7×5	15 $20 \div 2$	23 $21 \div 3$
8 6×2	16 $27 \div 3$	24 $20 \div 4$

C

1 42	5 43	9 11
2 125	6 130	10 19
3 54	7 6	11 52
4 59	8 9	12 54

13

$\times$	2	3	4
10	20	30	40
6	12	18	24
4	8	12	16

14

$\times$	3	4	10
7	21	28	70
2	6	8	20
9	27	36	90

15

$\times$	4	3	5
3	12	9	15
8	32	24	40
5	20	15	25

page 53

A

1 16	9 90	17 250	25 92
2 20	10 60	18 65	26 58
3 30	11 11	19 300	27 24
4 28	12 20	20 75	28 34
5 34	13 9	21 46	29 26
6 800	14 13	22 56	30 37
7 70	15 16	23 74	31 43
8 50	16 85	24 70	32 49

B

1 32	9 4400	17 340	25 134
2 42	10 7800	18 2800	26 118
3 68	11 21	19 1800	27 81
4 54	12 32	20 3700	28 67
5 460	13 44	21 128	29 79
6 760	14 27	22 112	30 89
7 980	15 380	23 156	31 58
8 880	16 470	24 186	32 87

C

1 31	9 184	17 286	25 122
2 42	10 152	18 312	26 169
3 68	11 118	19 334	27 128
4 92	12 108	20 348	28 177
5 760	13 1540	21 276	29 196
6 690	14 1960	22 358	30 148
7 3900	15 14 600	23 370	31 159
8 580	16 17 200	24 394	32 188

pages 54 and 55

A

2 24	5 60	8 80
3 32	6 92	9 120
4 44	7 60	10 200

11 7	12 11	13 8	14 20
14	22	4	10
28	44	2	5
56	88		
112	176		

B

2 56	7 230	12 117
3 96	8 240	13 182
4 128	9 320	14 247
5 170	10 460	15 299
6 390	11 78	16 338

17 16	19 24	21 20
8	12	10
4	6	5
18 100	20 60	22 500
50	30	250
25	15	125

C

1 240	4 238	7 234	10 225	13 625
2 630	5 496	8 176	11 375	14 550
3 1200	6 2300	9 1950	12 325	15 725

16 64	21 9	26 2
17 $7\frac{1}{2}$	22 $12\frac{1}{2}$	27 5
18 16	23 21	28 9
19 $4\frac{1}{2}$	24 $8\frac{1}{2}$	29 6
20 19	25 13	30 13

31 35	35 8	37 12	39 14
32 23	4	6	7
33 125	36 300	38 30	40 5
34 95	150	15	$2\frac{1}{2}$

page 56

A

1 30	9 60	17 3	25 48
2 12	10 48	18 10	26 18
3 42	11 2	19 5	27 54
4 24	12 8	20 9	28 0
5 0	13 4	21 24	29 30
6 36	14 6	22 6	30 60
7 54	15 1	23 42	
8 6	16 7	24 12	

B

1 18	7 30	13 4
2 60	8 0	14 8
3 42	9 48	15 5
4 54	10 6	16 9
5 36	11 1	17 3
6 12	12 10	18 7

19 3×6	25 5×6	31 $42 \div 6$
20 7×6	26 9×6	32 $6 \div 6$
21 4×6	27 $30 \div 6$	33 $54 \div 6$
22 6×6	28 $48 \div 6$	34 $36 \div 6$
23 0×6	29 $60 \div 6$	
24 8×6	30 $24 \div 6$	

C

1 240	12 100	23 60
2 1200	13 40	24 24
3 3000	14 1000	25 96
4 420	15 600	26 72
5 180	16 50	27 48
6 4800	17 800	28 108
7 2400	18 300	29 84
8 4200	19 70	30 240
9 540	20 900	31 144
10 3600	21 36	32 16
11 20	22 120	

page 57

A

1 21	11 4	21 14
2 14	12 2	22 35
3 35	13 10	23 63
4 7	14 1	24 7
5 56	15 6	25 21
6 0	16 3	26 42
7 49	17 9	27 0
8 28	18 7	28 28
9 63	19 5	29 70
10 42	20 8	30 56

B

1 35	4 0	7 56	10 3	13 2		16 9
2 14	5 63	8 42	11 10	14 6		17 4
3 28	6 49	9 70	12 8	15 5		18 7

19 2×7	25 9×7	31 $63 \div 7$
20 5×7	26 7×7	32 $42 \div 7$
21 8×7	27 $21 \div 7$	33 $7 \div 7$
22 3×7	28 $49 \div 7$	34 $56 \div 7$
23 6×7	29 $14 \div 7$	
24 4×7	30 $35 \div 7$	

C

1 140	12 40	23 84
2 350	13 20	24 126
3 560	14 800	25 42
4 2800	15 50	26 112
5 1400	16 300	27 420
6 490	17 60	28 56
7 2100	18 90	29 98
8 630	19 1000	30 840
9 4200	20 700	31 32 weeks
10 5600	21 70	32 91
11 70	22 28	33 343

page 58

A

1 40	11 3	21 24
2 16	12 10	22 48
3 80	13 8	23 16
4 32	14 2	24 0
5 72	15 6	25 80
6 56	16 1	26 8
7 8	17 5	27 32
8 64	18 9	28 72
9 0	19 4	29 40
10 48	20 7	30 56

B

1 24	4 0	7 56	10 5	13 9	16 8
2 80	5 72	8 6	11 10	14 6	17 4
3 48	6 32	9 64	12 3	15 1	18 7

19 5×8	27 $24 \div 8$
20 3×8	28 $56 \div 8$
21 6×8	29 $8 \div 8$
22 2×8	30 $32 \div 8$
23 9×8	31 $64 \div 8$
24 7×8	32 $48 \div 8$
25 4×8	33 $40 \div 8$
26 8×8	34 $72 \div 8$

C

1 320	9 640	17 100	25 144
2 160	10 4800	18 700	26 96
3 5600	11 40	19 90	27 128
4 2400	12 20	20 500	28 64
5 400	13 600	21 32	29 320
6 1600	14 30	22 80	30 480
7 720	15 400	23 112	31 26
8 4000	16 80	24 48	32 232 miles

page 59

A

1 27	9 0	17 9	25 36
2 90	10 72	18 3	26 0
3 63	11 4	19 8	27 90
4 9	12 7	20 6	28 27
5 45	13 2	21 45	29 54
6 18	14 5	22 18	30 72
7 54	15 10	23 9	
8 81	16 1	24 63	

B

1 36	4 90	7 81	10 3	13 6	16 7
2 72	5 0	8 45	11 5	14 2	17 10
3 9	6 54	9 63	12 9	15 4	18 8

19 6×9	25 5×9	31 $63 \div 9$
20 4×9	26 7×9	32 $9 \div 9$
21 9×9	27 $36 \div 9$	33 $54 \div 9$
22 10×9	28 $90 \div 9$	34 $81 \div 9$
23 3×9	29 $72 \div 9$	
24 8×9	30 $27 \div 9$	

C

1 270	9 4500	17 1000	25 90
2 450	10 8100	18 80	26 144
3 630	11 30	19 200	27 360
4 180	12 50	20 700	28 72
5 2700	13 20	21 54	29 162
6 3600	14 90	22 108	30 126
7 720	15 40	23 36	31 324
8 540	16 600	24 540	32 17

page 60 (multiplying by 9 or 11)

A

1 36	3 54	5 72	7 81	9 63
2 33	4 55	6 77	8 66	10 88

B

1 108	3 144	5 117	7 171	9 135
2 143	4 187	6 165	8 132	10 209

c

1	133 ÷ 19	6	273 ÷ 21
2	126 ÷ 21	7	304 ÷ 19
3	209 ÷ 19	8	378 ÷ 21
4	189 ÷ 21	9	361 ÷ 19
5	266 ÷ 19	10	441 ÷ 21

page 60 (partitioning)

A

1	28	3	34	5	46	7	52	9	64
2	65	4	80	6	95	8	110	10	125

B

1	36	3	57	5	69	7	81	9	105
2	52	4	68	6	88	8	126	10	136

c

1	128 ÷ 4	5	200 ÷ 8	9	288 ÷ 6
2	230 ÷ 5	6	252 ÷ 9	10	161 ÷ 7
3	222 ÷ 6	7	156 ÷ 4		
4	112 ÷ 7	8	265 ÷ 5		

page 61 (multiplying a multiple of 10)

A

1	60	5	120	9	160
2	80	6	100	10	60
3	200	7	100	11	250
4	150	8	90	12	120

B

1	150	5	30 × 3	9	20 × 9
2	240	6	20 × 5	10	80 × 5
3	360	7	40 × 7	11	60 × 4
4	350	8	70 × 3	12	50 × 6

c

1

×6
90 → 540
60 → 360
80 → 480
50 → 300
30 → 180

3

×8
80 → 640
60 → 480
30 → 240
90 → 720
70 → 560

2

×7
60 → 420
70 → 490
50 → 350
80 → 560
40 → 280

4

×9
50 → 450
80 → 720
40 → 360
90 → 810
70 → 630

page 61 (multiplying two-digit numbers)

A

1	24	5	28	9	36
2	55	6	66	10	84
3	84	7	48	11	69
4	39	8	68	12	88

B

1	32	5	13 × 5	9	14 × 4
2	115	6	25 × 2	10	22 × 5
3	72	7	17 × 3	11	25 × 3
4	45	8	19 × 2	12	21 × 4

c

1

×6
43 → 258
57 → 342
38 → 228
31 → 186
42 → 252

3

×8
35 → 280
48 → 384
63 → 504
55 → 440
24 → 192

2

×7
24 → 168
19 → 133
36 → 252
71 → 497
43 → 301

4

×9
18 → 162
37 → 333
72 → 648
51 → 459
44 → 396

page 62

A

1	40	6	100	11	15	16	45
2	60	7	140	12	40	17	30
3	70	8	120	13	25	18	10
4	80	9	30	14	35	19	50
5	90	10	130	15	20	20	100
21	50p	23	£100	25	£2·40		
22	£300	24	60p	26	£200		

B

1	50	9	55	17	70 ÷ 2
2	70	10	90	18	120 ÷ 2
3	80	11	65	19	190 ÷ 2
4	110	12	75	20	130 ÷ 2
5	160	13	20 × 2	21	×
6	170	14	45 × 2	22	÷
7	70	15	65 × 2	23	÷
8	35	16	80 × 2	24	×

c

1

Double
75 → 150
125 → 250
160 → 320
255 → 510
380 → 760
475 → 950

3

Halve
260 → 130
420 → 210
770 → 385
690 → 345
580 → 290
850 → 425

2

Double
95 → 190
170 → 340
315 → 630
435 → 870
260 → 520
395 → 790

4

Halve
320 → 160
470 → 235
740 → 370
910 → 455
630 → 315
890 → 445

5	170	7	54	9	85
6	330	8	135	10	6

page 63 (multiplying by 10/100)

A

1	30	5	90	9	500
2	70	6	900	10	700
3	50	7	400		
4	80	8	800		

B

1
×10
42 → 420
315 → 3150
66 → 660
429 → 4290
54 → 540
218 → 2180
672 → 6720
51 → 510
196 → 1960
537 → 5370

2
×100
16 → 1600
43 → 4300
9 → 900
25 → 2500
71 → 7100
4 → 400
57 → 5700
32 → 3200
86 → 8600
64 → 6400

C

1 2530 5 35 × 100 9 127 × 10
2 8400 6 530 × 10 10 102 × 100
3 1080 7 671 × 10
4 24 600 8 430 × 100

page 63 (dividing multiples of 1000)

A

1 20 5 90 9 5
2 7 6 7 10 9
3 40 7 3
4 80 8 6

B

1
÷10
3000 → 300
6000 → 600
9000 → 900
500 → 50
1000 → 100
8000 → 800
200 → 20
7000 → 700
300 → 30
4000 → 400

2
÷100
5000 → 50
2000 → 20
7000 → 70
300 → 3
9000 → 90
1000 → 10
500 → 5
4000 → 40
8000 → 80
600 → 6

C

1 320 6 67 ÷ 100
2 70 7 4600 ÷ 10
3 18 8 719 × 100
4 500 9 4000 ÷ 10
5 2300 ÷ 10 10 780 ÷ 10

page 64

A

1 28 5 95 9 140
2 45 6 54 10 100
3 85 7 96 11 165
4 52 8 58 12 108

B

1 48 9 192
2 130 10 288
3 78 11 301
4 147 12 264
5 112 13 268
6 141 14 405
7 245 15 168
8 235 16 216

C

1 508 7 966 13 1440
2 645 8 2056 14 3752
3 1498 9 972 15 1372
4 1224 10 2925 16 2565
5 1344 11 1488 17 2250
6 1476 12 1503 18 4664

page 65

A

1 34 5 52 9 112
2 69 6 95 10 105
3 60 7 54
4 105 8 230

B

1 134 5 195 9 112
2 104 6 177 10 148
3 192 7 166
4 287 8 140
11 184 15 174 19 320
12 365 16 204 20 156
13 200 17 371
14 171 18 208

C

1 1840 7 1176 13 2365
2 2516 8 1794 14 2303
3 548 9 3488 15 2214
4 1715 10 1422 16 3176
5 942 11 1908
6 2925 12 1456

page 66

A

1 **13** 5 14 9 18 13 13
2 12 6 13 10 19 14 19
3 16 7 17 11 15 15 17
4 15 8 16 12 19 16 18

B

1 14 7 16 r 5 13 18 r 1
2 16 r 2 8 17 r 3 14 18 r 1
3 18 r 1 9 15 r 4 15 12 r 3
4 14 r 3 10 15 r 5 16 17 r 7
5 18 r 2 11 18 r 4 17 £87
6 17 r 3 12 12 r 6

C

1 25 r 4 5 33 r 1 9 44 r 1 13 57 r 5
2 35 r 3 6 46 r 1 10 57 r 2 14 73 r 2
3 27 r 5 7 47 r 2 11 54 r 5 15 64 r 4
4 34 r 7 8 43 r 1 12 65 r 6 16 77 r 7
17 39 18 28 19 36 20 52

page 67

A

1 12 5 13 9 12 13 13
2 16 6 15 10 16 14 15
3 14 7 18 11 19 15 18
4 19 8 17 12 14 16 17
17 14 18 18 19 16 20 17

B

1 18	**5** 23	**9** 24	**13** 28
2 19	**6** 12	**10** 18	**14** 17
3 16	**7** 34	**11** 34	**15** 29
4 14	**8** 14	**12** 17	**16** 22
17 21	**18** 25	**19** 135	

C

1 19	**5** 21	**9** 27	**13** 24
2 21	**6** 15	**10** 23	**14** 31
3 22	**7** 18 r 5	**11** 29	**15** 23 r 7
4 18	**8** 25	**12** 22	**16** 34
17 28	**18** 45 litres	**19** 44	

page 68 (number operations)

A

1 +	**3** ×	**5** ÷	**7** +
2 −	**4** −	**6** ÷	**8** ×

B

1 +	**3** +	**5** ×	**7** ×
2 ÷	**4** −	**6** ÷	**8** −

C

1 −	**3** −	**5** ×	**7** +
2 ×	**4** +	**6** ÷	**8** ÷

page 70

A

1 41	**3** 40	**5** 48	**7** 83	**9** 96
2 19	**4** 12	**6** 24	**8** 13	**10** 8

B

1 60	**3** 121	**5** 98	**7** 101	**9** 176
2 38 secs.	**4** 8	**6** 63	**8** 84	**10** 45

C

1 56	**3** 160	**5** 86	**7** 541	**9** £26
2 295	**4** 5	**6** 48	**8** 672	**10** 50

pages 72 and 73

A

1 217p	**7** £0·68	**13** £4·50	**19** £3·80
2 428p	**8** £8·92	**14** £2·25	**20** £2·20
3 760p	**9** £3·50	**15** 10	**21** 90p
4 943p	**10** £2·30	**16** £1·10	**22** £1·70
5 £1·79	**11** £3·24	**17** 30p	
6 £3·56	**12** £1·75	**18** £1·50	

23 20p, 20p, 2p, 1p	**29** 20p, 5p, 2p, 2p
24 50p, 5p, 2p, 1p	**30** £1, 5p, 2p
25 50p, 20p, 10p, 5p	**31** £3, 50p, 20p, 20p
26 20p, 10p, 5p, 2p	**32** 50p, 20p, 2p, 2p
27 £2, 50p, 10p	**33** 50p, 20p, 20p, 2p
28 50p, 10p, 5p, 1p	**34** £2, £2, 20p, 10p, 5p

B

1 830p	**3** 1351p	**5** £6·37	**7** £8·30
2 428p	**4** 1107p	**6** £5·06	**8** £11·41

9 £3·13, £6·87	**12** £3·55, £6·45
10 £4·80, £5·20	**13** £4·50, £5·50
11 £8·50, £1·50	**14** £2·88, £7·12
15 6	**17** Hot chocolate
16 90p	**18** 95p

C

1 1642p	**3** 3105p	**5** £9·09	**7** £38·07
2 4098p	**4** 1700p	**6** £20·83	**8** £100·16

9 £10·65, £9·35	**12** £17·99, £2·01
10 £8·46, £11·54	**13** £16·70, £3·30
11 £15·11, £4·89	**14** £19·60, £0·40
15 23	**16** 95p	**17** coke	**18** 85p

pages 74 and 75

A

1 500 m	**5** $3\frac{1}{2}$ km	**9** 600 cm
2 3000 m	**6** $4\frac{1}{2}$ km	**10** 4 m
3 2000 m	**7** 50 cm	**11** $3\frac{1}{2}$ m
4 5 km	**8** 200 cm	**12** 8 m

13 cm	**14** m	**15** km	**16** cm	**17** m	**18** mm
21 5 km	**23** 40 cm	**25** 200 cm			
22 $\frac{1}{2}$ m	**24** $\frac{1}{2}$ km	**26** 4 km			

B

1 1500 m	**5** 75 cm	**9** 5 mm
2 250 m	**6** 250 cm	**10** 1 mm
3 2750 m	**7** 30 cm	**11** 7 mm
4 1100 m	**8** 360 cm	**12** 29 mm
13 m	**15** cm	**17** km
14 mm	**16** m	**18** cm

23 =	**24** >	**25** <	**26** >	**27** =	**28** >

C

1

mm	cm
3	→ $\frac{3}{10}$
18	→ $1\frac{8}{10}$
9	→ $\frac{9}{10}$
147	→ $14\frac{7}{10}$

3

m	km
720	→ $\frac{72}{100}$
4600	→ $4\frac{6}{10}$
3500	→ $3\frac{1}{2}$
2790	→ $2\frac{79}{100}$

2

cm	m
290	→ $2\frac{9}{10}$
84	→ $\frac{84}{100}$
175	→ $1\frac{3}{4}$
406	→ $4\frac{6}{100}$

4

m	cm
$\frac{37}{100}$	→ 37
$1\frac{9}{10}$	→ 190
$3\frac{2}{100}$	→ 302
$1\frac{45}{100}$	→ 145

5 10 mm	**7** 4 km	**9** 50 mm
6 3000 cm	**8** 50 cm	**10** 20 m

11 $\frac{6}{10}$ cm, 26 mm, 6 cm, $\frac{2}{10}$ m

12 700 cm, 70 m, $\frac{7}{10}$ km, 7000 m

13 4000 mm, $\frac{4}{100}$ km, 44 m, 400 m

14 $\frac{3}{10}$ m, 31 cm, 13 m, $\frac{3}{100}$ km

page 76

A

1 71 cm	**3** 8	**5** 380 m
2 48 m	**4** 80 cm	

B

1 1 m 44 cm	**3** 10 cm	**5** 4 cm
2 3 m 20 cm	**4** 1·5 m	

C

1 6 km	**3** 25 cm	**5** 53 cm
2 86 cm	**4** 1 m 5 cm	

page 77

A

1 a) 15 cm, 45 cm
  b) 30 cm
2 a) 45 cm, 55 cm
  b) 10 cm
3 a) 2 kg, 8 kg
  b) 6 kg
4 a) 40 g, 90 g
  b) 50 g
5 a) 1 l, 3 l
  b) 2 l

6 a) 150 ml, 250 ml
  b) 100 ml
7 a) 53 kg, 65 kg
  b) 12 kg
8 a) 440 g, 520 g
  b) 80 g
9 a) 650 ml, 850 ml
  b) 200 ml
10 a) 100 ml, 150 ml
  b) 50 ml

B

1 a) 5 kg, 20 kg
  b) 15 kg
2 a) 30 g, 70 g
  b) 40 g
3 a) 10 mm, 16 mm
  b) 6 mm
4 a) 15 cm, 45 cm
  b) 30 cm
5 a) 0·25 l, 0·5 l
  b) 0·25 l

6 a) 50 ml, 175 ml
  b) 125 ml
7 a) 280 g, 370 g
  b) 90 g
8 a) 17 cm, 28 cm
  b) 11 cm
9 a) 300 ml, 600 ml
  b) 300 ml
10 a) 0·5 l, 1 l
  b) 0·5 l

C

1 a) 1 cm, 2·5 cm
  b) 1·5 cm
2 a) 22·5 kg, 24·5 kg
  b) 2 kg
3 a) 2·3 kg, 2·8 kg
  b) 0·5 kg
4 a) 70 cm, 90 cm
  b) 20 cm
5 a) 1·3 l, 2·5 l
  b) 1·2 l

6 a) 100 ml, 460 ml
  b) 360 ml
7 a) 4·6 kg, 5·8 kg
  b) 1·2 kg
8 a) 140 g, 180 g
  b) 40 g
9 a) 0·25 l, 0·75 l
  b) 0·5 l
10 a) 75 ml, 165 ml
  b) 90 ml

page 78

A

1 1000 g
2 2000 g
3 1 kg
4 $2\frac{1}{2}$ kg

5 500 g
6 2500 g
7 4 kg
8 $1\frac{1}{2}$ kg

9 3000 g
10 6500 g
11 5 kg
12 $4\frac{1}{2}$ kg

13 grams
14 kg
15 grams
16 kg

B

1 2000 g
2 1500 g
3 $\frac{1}{4}$ kg
4 $1\frac{3}{4}$ kg

5 750 g
6 1700 g
7 $3\frac{2}{10}$ kg
8 $4\frac{1}{2}$ kg

9 3250 g
10 900 g
11 $6\frac{8}{10}$ kg
12 $9\frac{1}{4}$ kg

13 kg
14 grams
15 kg
16 grams

C

1

g	kg
3000 →	3
2750 →	$2\frac{3}{4}$
1560 →	$1\frac{56}{100}$
2250 →	$2\frac{1}{4}$
3100 →	$3\frac{1}{10}$
1820 →	$1\frac{82}{100}$

2

kg	g
$5\frac{2}{10}$ →	5200
$1\frac{1}{4}$ →	1250
$2\frac{48}{100}$ →	2480
$2\frac{3}{10}$ →	2300
$4\frac{3}{4}$ →	4750
$5\frac{17}{100}$ →	5170

3 150 g
4 $\frac{3}{4}$ kg

5 1 g
6 40 g

page 79

A

1 32 kg
2 160 g

3 77 kg
4 200 g

5 360 g

B

1 250 g
2 20

3 $2\frac{4}{10}$ kg
4 800 g

5 8 kg

C

1 $3\frac{3}{4}$ kg
2 25

3 3 kg 800 g
4 1 kg 300 g

5 3 kg

page 80

A

1 1000 ml
2 2000 ml
3 1 l
4 $1\frac{1}{2}$ l

5 500 ml
6 2500 ml
7 3 l
8 $3\frac{1}{2}$ l

9 5500 ml
10 7000 ml
11 6 l
12 $4\frac{1}{2}$ l

13 ml
14 litres
15 litres
16 ml

B

1 1500 ml
2 250 ml
3 2 l
4 $1\frac{1}{4}$ l

5 1750 ml
6 3700 ml
7 $2\frac{1}{2}$ l
8 $\frac{6}{10}$ l

9 2250 ml
10 300 ml
11 $4\frac{3}{4}$ l
12 $9\frac{1}{10}$ l

13 litres
14 ml
15 ml
16 litres

C

1

ml	litres
5000 →	5
1200 →	$1\frac{2}{10}$
3500 →	$3\frac{1}{2}$
2000 →	2
750 →	$\frac{3}{4}$
2250 →	$2\frac{1}{4}$

2

litres	ml
$1\frac{8}{10}$ →	1800
$4\frac{1}{2}$ →	4500
$1\frac{3}{10}$ →	1300
$2\frac{3}{4}$ →	2750
$\frac{1}{4}$ →	250
$\frac{9}{10}$ →	900

3 5000 ml
4 200 ml

5 30 ml
6 3000 l

page 81

A

1 160 l
2 300 ml

3 70 ml
4 700 ml

5 260 ml

B

1 1 l 500 ml
2 100 ml

3 20
4 3 l 200 ml

5 350 ml

C

1 10
2 2 l 150 ml

3 4 l
4 1 l 800 ml

5 75 ml

page 82

A

1 12 cm
2 14 cm
3 12 cm
4 a) 20 cm²
  b) 18 cm
5 a) 36 cm²
  b) 24 cm

6 a) 24 cm²
  b) 22 cm
7 a) 64 cm²
  b) 32 cm
8 16 cm
9 24 cm²
10 16 cm

B

1 12 cm
2 12 cm
3 12 cm
4 N 16 sqs., M 16 sqs., O 14 sqs., Z 11 sqs.

C

1

Length	8 cm	6 cm	7 cm	10 cm	15 cm	8 cm
Width	4 cm	3 cm	2 cm	7 cm	9 cm	5 cm
Perimeter	24 cm	18 cm	18 cm	34 cm	48 cm	26 cm
Area	32 cm^2	18 cm^2	14 cm^2	70 cm^2	135 cm^2	40 cm^2

4 10 000   5 £180   6 6

pages 84 and 85

A

1 300 mins.
2 90 mins.
3 2 mins
4 $\frac{1}{2}$ min.
5 14 days
6 35 days
7 2 days
8 10 days
9 1 year
10 50 years
11 2 years
12 2 years
14 31
15 a) Wednesday
   b) Friday
16 5
17 14th December
18 Saturday

B

1 480 mins.
2 135 mins.
3 6 mins.
4 1$\frac{1}{2}$ mins.
5 28 days
6 42 days
7 1$\frac{1}{2}$ days
8 5 days
9 60 years
10 200 years
11 3 years
12 1$\frac{1}{2}$ years
13 31
14 30
15 29
16 61
17 61
18 62
19 23
20 27th August

C

1 540 mins.
2 165 mins.
3 8 mins.
4 2$\frac{1}{4}$ mins.
5 26 weeks
6 208 weeks
7 6 weeks
8 5200 weeks
9 4 years
10 1$\frac{1}{2}$ years
11 150 years
12 500 years
13 Monday
14 Saturday
15 Sunday
16 Sunday
17 6th September
18 22nd October
19

AUGUST						
Su	M	Tu	W	Th	F	Sa
1	2	3	4	5	6	7
8	9	10	11	12	13	14
15	16	17	18	19	20	21
22	23	24	25	26	27	28
29	30	31				

pages 86 and 87

A

1 a) half past 8   b) 8:30 a.m.
2 a) quarter past 6   b) 6:15 p.m.
3 a) 5 to 2   b) 1:55 a.m.
4 a) quarter to 5   b) 4:45 p.m.
5 a) 10 past 2   b) 2:10 p.m.
6 a) 25 to 8   b) 7:35 a.m.
7 a) 10 to 9   b) 8:50 p.m.
8 a) 5 past 3   b) 3:05 a.m.
9 a) 9 o' clock   b) 9:00 a.m.
10 a) 20 past 5   b) 5:20 p.m.
11 a) 2 minutes to 5   b) 4:58 a.m.
12 a) 20 to 11   b) 10:40 a.m.

B

1 a) 11 mins. to 9   b) 8:49 a.m.
2 a) 3 mins. to 4   b) 3:57 p.m.
3 a) 18 mins. past 1   b) 1:18 a.m.
4 a) 27 mins. to 12   b) 11:33 a.m.
5 a) 21 mins. past 6   b) 6:21 a.m.
6 a) 4 mins. past 9   b) 9:04 p.m.
7 a) 14 mins to 11   b) 10:46 a.m.
8 a) 8 mins to 6   b) 5:52 p.m.
9 8:24 a.m., 3:32 p.m., 0:53 a.m., 11:08 a.m., 5:56 a.m., 8:39 p.m., 10:21 a.m., 5:27 p.m.
10 12:49 p.m., 7:57 p.m., 5:18 a.m., 3:33 p.m., 10:21 a.m., 1:04 a.m., 2:46 p.m., 9:52 p.m.

C

1

TIME IN WORDS	12-HOUR CLOCK	24-HOUR CLOCK
half past eight	8:30 p.m.	20:30
6 mins. past 7	7:06 a.m.	07:06
13 mins. to 12	11:47 a.m.	11:47
6 mins. to 10	9:54 p.m.	21:54
25 past 4	4:25 a.m.	04:25
17 mins. to 4	3:43 p.m.	15:43
9 mins. past 8	8:09 a.m.	08:09
11 mins. past 1	1:11 p.m.	13:11
28 mins. past 1	1:28 a.m.	01:28
28 mins. to 5	4:32 p.m.	16:32

2 a) 20:46   b) 19:50
   07:22   06:26
   12:03   11:07
   22:10   21:14
   04:41   03:45
   15:59   15:03
   08:25   07:29
   13:27   12:31
   01:44   00:48
   16:48   15:52

3 a) 4 h 30 mins.   c) 3 h 50 mins.
   b) 9 h 55 mins.   d) 4 h 40 mins.

pages 88 and 89

A

1 10 mins.   **5** National News
2 25 mins.   **6** Points of View
3 30 mins.   **7** Gardener's World
4 30 mins.   **8** Tennis
9 Blue Peter, Wheel of Fortune
10 Weather, Local News
11 Tennis, Carry On Nurse
12 Eastenders, Coronation Street
13

	Bus 1	Bus 2	Bus 3	Bus 4	Bus 5	Bus 6
Station	9:00	9:15	9:30	9:45	10:00	10:15
Hospital	9:20	9:35	9:50	10:05	10:20	10:35

14 a) Bus 1   c) Bus 4
    b) Bus 5   d) Bus 6

B

1 25 mins.   **3** 1 h 15 mins.   **5** 2 h 30 mins.
2 20 mins.   **4** 25 mins.   **6** 1 h 45 mins.
7 Doctor Who, Home and Away
8 Blue Peter, Wheel of Fortune
9 Sports Quiz, Local News
10 Gardener's World, Coronation Street
11

	Bus 1	Bus 2	Bus 3	Bus 4	Bus 5	Bus 6
Village	9:15	9:35	9:55	10:15	10:35	10:55
Superstore	9:50	10:10	10:30	10:50	11:10	11:30

C

1 50 mins.   **7** Home and Away
2 1 h 25 mins.   **8** Wish You Were Here
3 35 mins.   **9** Gardener's World
4 1 h 28 mins.   **10** Carry on Nurse
5 2 h 25 mins.   **11** Eastenders
6 4 h 25 mins.   **12** Local News

13

	Train 1	Train 2	Train 3	Train 4	Train 5	Train 6
Oldport	8:00	8:47	9:23	9:56	10:34	11:09
Highcliff	8:06	8:53	9:29	10:02	10:40	11:15
Whitehill	8:19	9:06	9:42	10:15	10:53	11:28
Westham	8:38	9:25	10:01	10:34	11:12	11:47
City Centre	8:45	9:32	10:08	10:41	11:19	11:54

page 90

A

1 40 mins.   **3** 7:20   **5** 4:10
2 8:45   **4** 10:45

B

1 43 mins.   **3** 3:35   **5** 3:10
2 8:10   **4** 4:40

C

1 5 h 35 mins.   **4** 13:55
2 06:30   **5** 15:15
3 3 h 40 mins.

page 93

A

No.	Sides	Polygon
1	6	hexagon
2	4	quadrilateral
3	3	triangle
4	7	heptagon
5	4	quadrilateral
6	3	triangle
7	6	hexagon
8	4	quadrilateral
9	3	triangle
10	5	pentagon
11	4	quadrilateral
12	8	octagon
13	4	quadrilateral
14	3	triangle
15	5	pentagon
16	8	octagon

B

1
  1 regular hexagon
  2 irregular quadrilateral
  3 equilateral triangle
  4 irregular heptagon
  5 square
  6 right-angled triangle
  7 irregular hexagon
  8 rectangle
  9 irregular triangle
  10 irregular pentagon
  11 square
  12 regular octagon
  13 rectangle
  14 isosceles triangle
  15 regular pentagon
  16 irregular octagon

2 4 and 16 are concave

C

1

No.	Shape	Equal sides	Equal angles
1	regular hexagon	6	6
2	irregular quadrilateral	0	0
3	equilateral triangle	3	3
4	irregular heptagon	0	0
5	square	4	4
6	right-angled triangle	0	0
7	irregular hexagon	0	0
8	rectangle	2 pairs	4
9	irregular triangle	0	0
10	irregular pentagon	0	0
11	square	4	4
12	regular octagon	8	8
13	rectangle	2 pairs	4
14	isosceles triangle	2	2
15	regular pentagon	5	5
16	irregular octagon	0	0

2 square
3 equilateral triangle

pages 94 and 95

B

1
  1 hexagonal prism
  2 hemi-sphere
  3 square based pyramid
  4 cube
  5 cone
  6 pentagonal prism
  7 tetrahedron
  8 cylinder
  9 cuboid
  10 triangular prism
  11 sphere
  12 octagonal prism

2 hemi-sphere, cone, cylinder, sphere (Shapes 2, 5, 8, 11)

3 triangular prism, cube, cuboid, pentagonal prism, hexagonal prism, octagonal prism (Shapes 1, 4, 6, 9, 10, 12)

C

No.	Shape	Flat Faces	Edges	Vertices
1	hexagonal prism	8	18	12
3	square based pyramid	5	8	5
4	cube	6	12	8
6	pentagonal prism	7	15	10
7	tetrahedron	4	6	4
9	cuboid	6	12	8
10	triangular prism	5	9	6
12	octagonal prism	10	24	16

page 97

B

1 6		**6** 12		**11** 10	
2 6		**7** 7		**12** 6	
3 8		**8** 9		**13** 7	
4 6		**9** 8		**14** 8	
5 8		**10** 7		**15** 9	

C

1 3		**6** 4		**11** 2	
2 6		**7** 9		**12** 6	
3 8		**8** 11		**13** 13	
4 10		**9** 24		**14** 4	
5 4		**10** 17		**15** 9	

page 98

A

1 B W D M   **4** D F
2 H X O   **5** A C
3 N F K R Z   **6** B E

page 101

A

1 24

2 a) 8, Double 4
    b) 2, Double 1
    c) 2, Double 2
    d) Double 6, Treble 4

3 6

4 a) Treble 3
    b) Double 7
    c) Treble 7
    d) Double 5
    e) Treble 5
    f) Double 8

5 11, 13, 17, 19

Answers

B
1 48
2 a) D5 + T8 b) T5 + T8
     D8 + T6   T6 + T7
3 a) T8 + D6 b) T8 + T3 c) T8 + 8 d) T8 + 5
     T8 + T4   T7 + D6   T8 + D4   T7 + 8
     T7 + T5   T7 + T4   T6 + D7   T7 + D4
     T6 + T6   T6 + T5   D8 + D8   T5 + D7
4 a) T7 + D7 b) T7 + D8 c) T8 + D7 d) T8 + D8

C
1 72   3 T8 + T8 + D5   4 65, 67, 68
2 T8 + T7 + D7   T7 + T7 + D8
                         T8 + T6 + D8

pages 102 and 103
A
1 Easy work and good fun.
2 You have done this well.
3 A square
  B isosceles triangle
  C rectangle
  D right-angled triangle

B
1 Head east before going north.
2 Write your name like this.
3 M R N W

C
1 Across the room and up the stairs.

pages 106 and 107
A
1 (7, 6)   3 (5, 7)   5 (7, 1)   7 (8, 7)
2 (2, 3)   4 (7, 4)   6 (2, 6)   8 (6, 9)
10 a) Emford   c) Emford
   b) Charing   d) Ashdean

B
1 (5, 8)   3 (2, 6)   5 (8, 1)   7 (3, 1)
2 (6, 1)   4 (2, 5)   6 (2, 9)   8 (8, 7)
9 a) E   c) S   e) W   g) SE
  b) NW   d) NE   f) N   h) SW

C
1 (10, 4) 3 (7, 4)   5 (8, 3)   7 (10, 0)
2 (8, 4)   4 (5, 2)   6 (4, 8)   8 (5, 1)

pages 108 and 109
A
1 greater   5 right angle
2 right angle   6 less
3 less   7 greater
4 greater   8 right angle
9 6 o'clock   13 12 o'clock 17 6 o'clock
10 3 o'clock   14 6 o'clock   18 9 o'clock
11 12 o'clock 15 9 o'clock   19 12 o'clock
12 9 o'clock   16 3 o'clock   20 3 o'clock
21 180°   24 180°   27 180°
22 270°   25 90°   28 270°
23 90°   26 180°

B
5 1 o'clock   9 5 o'clock
6 4 o'clock   10 8 o'clock
7 12 o'clock   11 6 o'clock
8 11 o'clock   12 11 o'clock
13 45°   17 90°
14 180°   18 180°
15 90°   19 90°
16 45°   20 45°
21 ACDB

C
5 7 o'clock   9 5 o'clock
6 4 o'clock   10 12 o'clock
7 6 o'clock   11 8 o'clock
8 9 o'clock   12 3 o'clock
13 315°   17 225°
14 135°   18 315°
15 90°   19 90°
16 270°   20 135°
21 ABC   23 CAB
22 DBCA   24 DCAB
25 360°   26 a) 180°
                 b) 180°

pages 110 and 111
A
1

odd	not odd
3	12
5	18
17	4
19	6

2

triangles	not triangles
B	A
C	D
F	E
G	H

3

2-digit	not 2-digit
27	8
95	115
33	2
14	246

B
1

	odd	not odd
over 50	87 53 65	54 78 96
not over 50	31 37 45	48 16 22

2

	symmetrical	not symmetrical
triangles	C H	AF
not triangles	BE	DG

C

1

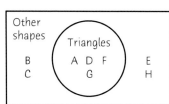

	2 digit nos.	not 2 digit nos.
multiples of 5	35 65 80	130 100 125
not multiples of 5	53 68 29	117 157 551

2

	concave	not concave
symmetrical	B E I	A F
not symmetrical	D G	C H

pages 112 and 113

A

1

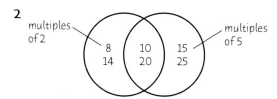

Other shapes

Triangles

B C | A D F G | E H

2

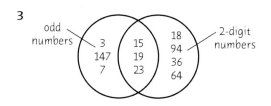

multiples of 2 | 8 14 | 10 20 | 15 25 | multiples of 5

3

odd numbers | 3 147 7 | 15 19 23 | 18 94 36 64 | 2-digit numbers

B

1

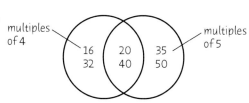

multiples of 4 | 16 32 | 20 40 | 35 50 | multiples of 5

2

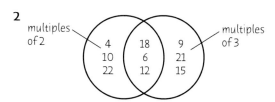

multiples of 2 | 4 10 22 | 18 6 12 | 9 21 15 | multiples of 3

3

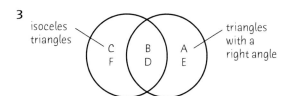

isoceles triangles | C F | B D | A E | triangles with a right angle

C

1

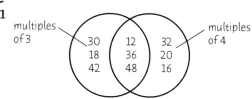

multiples of 3 | 30 18 42 | 12 36 48 | 32 20 16 | multiples of 4

2

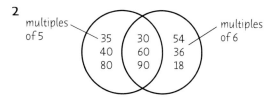

multiples of 5 | 35 40 80 | 30 60 90 | 54 36 18 | multiples of 6

3

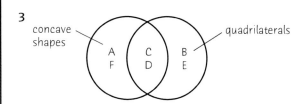

concave shapes | A F | C D | B E | quadrilaterals

pages 114 and 115

A

1

Goals	Frequency
0	4
1	4
2	9
3	5
4	2

2 a) 12   e) 4
b) 14   f) 6
c) Wednesday   g) 60
d) Friday   h) 12

B

1

Hours	Frequency
0	4
1	9
2	7
3	6
4	2

2 a) 25   d) mint
b) 10   e) 135
c) chocolate

C

1

Drink	Frequency
Orange	11
Cola	18
Lemonade	15
Blackcurrant	6

2 a) 250   d) 9 p.m. Too late for children.
b) 125   e) 1350
c) 25   f) Weekend. Large afternoon audiences.

pages 116 and 117

A

1

Game	Votes
Netball	5
Football	9
Rounders	4
Hockey	6

2 a) 8
  b) 7
  c) Red
  d) Green and Orange
  e) 5
  f) 4
  g) 30
  h) Kevin is right. 16 out of 30 is more than half.

B

1

No. of children	Total
1	6
2	12
3	9
4	3
5	2

2 a) E   e) I
  b) U   f) 10
  c) 50   g) 265
  d) 25

3

Vowel	Total
A	22
E	27
I	4
O	13
U	4

C

1

No. of letters	Words
2	14
3	9
4	9
5	6
6	4
7	6
8	2

2 a) 90   c) Saturday   e) 820
  b) 110   d) Tuesday

3

No. of letters	Words
1	6
2	17
3	27
4	25
5	19
6	11
7	9
8	1
9	0
10	2

page 118

A

1 three hundred and eight
2 one thousand two hundred and ninety-seven
3 four thousand three hundred and sixty-two
4 one thousand five hundred
5 two thousand six hundred and five
6 three thousand and eighty-nine
7 five thousand two hundred and forty
8 eight thousand and sixty

9 600	17 287	25 2235
10 70	18 420	26 4810
11 8	19 606	27 1497
12 5000	20 535	28 5063
13 80	21 2231	29 1480
14 6000	22 3369	30 530
15 4	23 5224	31 2170
16 500	24 4492	32 5700
33 250	37 200	41 861
34 7810	38 324	42 500
35 6900	39 39	43 180
36 4360	40 470	44 652

45 7198, 7981, 8197, 8719
46 1782, 1827, 2178, 2187
47 3469, 3496, 3649, 3694
48 1375, 1537, 1573, 1735

49 3, 6	53 70	57 600
50 6, 18	54 150	58 1000
51 5, 35	55 330	59 300
52 80, 40	56 290	60 800

61 A -7
   B -2
   C 4
   D 7

62 a) 5, 23, 47, 91
   b) 38, 54, 270, 316

63 10, 20, 30, 40, 50, 60	67 14, 18, 20, 60
64 6, 12, 18, 24, 30, 36	68 15, 18, 21, 60
65 4, 8, 12, 16, 20, 24	69 15, 20, 35, 60
66 9, 18, 27, 36, 45, 54	70 14, 21, 35, 49

page 119

1 $\frac{1}{6}$	13 $1 = \frac{3}{3}$	24 6
2 $\frac{2}{3}$	14 $\frac{1}{2} = \frac{5}{10}$	25 £4
3 $\frac{5}{8}$	15 $1 = \frac{10}{10}$	26 50 cm
4 $\frac{3}{10}$	16 $\frac{2}{3} = \frac{4}{6}$	27 $\frac{1}{2}$
5 $\frac{3}{4}$	17 $\frac{2}{5} = \frac{4}{10}$	28 $\frac{1}{10}$
6 $\frac{4}{5}$	18 $1 = \frac{8}{8}$	29 $\frac{1}{4}$
7 $\frac{1}{2} = \frac{4}{8}$	19 15	30 $\frac{1}{5}$
8 $\frac{1}{4} = \frac{4}{16}$	20 6	31 $\frac{1}{10}$
9 $\frac{1}{3} = \frac{2}{6}$	21 8p	32 $\frac{1}{2}$
10 $\frac{3}{5} = \frac{6}{10}$	22 5 cm	33 $\frac{1}{100}$
11 $\frac{1}{4} = \frac{2}{8}$	23 8	34 $\frac{1}{4}$
12 $\frac{1}{2} = \frac{3}{6}$		

35 $\frac{2}{10}$	39 $\frac{6}{10}$	43 $\frac{1}{10}$	47 $\frac{1}{2}$
36 6	40 8	44 $\frac{1}{4}$	48 $\frac{8}{10}$
37 $\frac{5}{10}$	41 10	45 $\frac{6}{10}$	49 $\frac{3}{4}$
38 10	42 $\frac{9}{10}$	46 $\frac{3}{10}$	50 $\frac{7}{10}$

51 0·5 55 0·4 59 A 0·2   60 0·7 64 0·3
52 0·2 56 0·25   B 0·6   61 0·9 65 0·5
53 1·0 57 0·3   C 1·4   62 1·8 66 1·1
54 0·9 58 0·75   D 1·8   63 1·7 67 1·6
68 1·5, 2·4, 4·2, 5·1   71 7, 7·9, 9, 9·7
69 3·3, 3·8, 8·3, 8·8   72 1·6, 6, 6·1, 16
70 4·5, 5·4, 45, 54

page 120
1 174   11 258 − 90   21 312
2 75   12 177 − 32   22 202
3 600 + 700   13 229   23 £4·86
4 156 + 44   14 293   24 £4·26
5 111 + 40   15 649   25 71
6 43 + 76   16 374   26 334
7 44   17 136   27 £2·73
8 436   18 336   28 £2·28
9 204 − 7   19 562   29 £105
10 1000 − 750 20 505   30 56 years
31 92   35 19 × 2   39 16 ÷ 1
32 132   36 5 × 7   40 27 ÷ 9
33 8 × 4   37 8   41 6000 ÷ 10
34 6 × 0   38 40   42 1920 ÷ 2
43 150   47 17   51 7 r 1
44 504   48 15   52 16 r 5
45 306   49 18   53 8 r 2
46 364   50 14   54 6 r 3
55 £21·50   59 120
56 £6·70   60 23
57 £8·25   61 161
58 £2·20   62 £16·50

page 121
1 1 m   5 1000 m   9 1 cm
2 50 cm   6 100 m   10 5 cm
3 10 cm   7 $\frac{1}{2}$ km   11 1000 g
4 $\frac{1}{4}$ m   8 1 mm   12 2 kg
13 $\frac{1}{10}$ kg   20 C 1$\frac{1}{2}$ kg, D 3 kg
14 500 g   21 E 1$\frac{1}{4}$ litres, F $\frac{1}{2}$ litre
15 $\frac{1}{2}$ litre   22 G 180 ml, H 40 ml
16 4000 ml   23 1 m 35 cm
17 1 litre   24 3 cm
18 100 ml   25 500 g
19 A 20, B 85 26 800 ml
27 8 cm²   36 80 yrs.
28 12 cm   37 156 weeks
31 35 days   38 1$\frac{1}{2}$ hours
32 3 mins.   39 30
33 2$\frac{1}{2}$ years   40 31
34 240 mins.   41 30
35 48 hours   42 31
43 a) 20 past 3   b) 3:20 p.m.
44 a) 22 mins. to 3 b) 2:38 a.m.
45 a) 9 mins. to 9   b) 8:51 a.m.
46 a) 14 mins. past 6 b) 6:14 p.m.
47 10:45
48 12:15

page 122
1 equilateral triangle   3 regular hexagon
2 quadrilateral   4 isosceles triangle

5 square   7 irregular pentagon
6 right-angled triangle 8 regular octagon
16 cone   20 hemi-sphere
17 tetrahedron   21 hexagonal prism
18 cuboid   22 7
19 cylinder   23 9
24 A (2,1)   E (1,3)
   B (4,5)   F (0,1)
   C (2,4)   G (5,4)
   D (4,0)
25 B   31 180°
26 F   32 90°
27 C   33 45°
28 G   34 180°
29 D   35 45°
30 B
36 3 o'clock   38 5 o'clock   40 10 o'clock
37 7 o'clock   39 8 o'clock

page 123
1
	even	not even
2-digits	58 92	15 81
	74	63
not 2-digits	4 150	7
	126 300	219

2
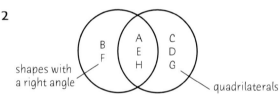
shapes with a right angle   quadrilaterals
B F | A E H | C D G

3
Method	Total
Walk	14
Bus	6
Car	8
Train	2

4 a) 10
  b) recorder
  c) 5
  d) 80

5
Meal	Total
Eggs	4
Meat	14
Fish	10
Salad	8

6 a) Red
  b) Green
  c) 25
  d) 25
  e) 145

page 124
A

6	9		2	7
3	5		3	0
		1	7	0	
6		5		1
1	7		3	8

B

1	4	■	6	8
2	8	■	1	9
6	■	8	5	■
■	2	1	■	2
1	5	■	9	4

C

4	9	3	■	6
8	7	■	9	0
■	■	7	2	■
6	9	■	5	4
3	2	0	■	9

page 125

A

1 $23 + 14$ 　 7 $45 + 28$ 　 13 $68 - 34$
2 $31 + 25$ 　 8 $26 + 15$ 　 14 $75 - 57$
3 $32 + 17$ 　 9 $46 - 33$ 　 15 $30 - 21$
4 $16 + 19$ 　 10 $38 - 17$ 　 16 $61 - 36$
5 $42 + 12$ 　 11 $57 - 41$
6 $28 + 33$ 　 12 $42 - 35$

B

1
$$\begin{array}{r} 32 \\ + 27 \\ \hline 59 \end{array}$$
5
$$\begin{array}{r} 58 \\ + 38 \\ \hline 96 \end{array}$$
9
$$\begin{array}{r} 75 \\ - 39 \\ \hline 36 \end{array}$$

2
$$\begin{array}{r} 53 \\ + 61 \\ \hline 114 \end{array}$$
6
$$\begin{array}{r} 37 \\ + 26 \\ \hline 63 \end{array}$$
10
$$\begin{array}{r} 57 \\ - 28 \\ \hline 29 \end{array}$$

3
$$\begin{array}{r} 45 \\ + 34 \\ \hline 79 \end{array}$$
7
$$\begin{array}{r} 48 \\ - 23 \\ \hline 25 \end{array}$$
11
$$\begin{array}{r} 92 \\ - 44 \\ \hline 48 \end{array}$$

4
$$\begin{array}{r} 58 \\ + 12 \\ \hline 70 \end{array}$$
8
$$\begin{array}{r} 67 \\ - 16 \\ \hline 51 \end{array}$$
12
$$\begin{array}{r} 42 \\ - 28 \\ \hline 14 \end{array}$$

C

1
$$\begin{array}{r} 436 \\ + 176 \\ \hline 612 \end{array}$$
5
$$\begin{array}{r} 518 \\ - 234 \\ \hline 284 \end{array}$$
9
$$\begin{array}{r} 89 \\ \times \ \ 2 \\ \hline 178 \end{array}$$

2
$$\begin{array}{r} 354 \\ + 298 \\ \hline 652 \end{array}$$
6
$$\begin{array}{r} 293 \\ - 175 \\ \hline 118 \end{array}$$
10
$$\begin{array}{r} 29 \\ \times \ \ 6 \\ \hline 174 \end{array}$$

3
$$\begin{array}{r} 273 \\ + 186 \\ \hline 459 \end{array}$$
7
$$\begin{array}{r} 24 \\ \times \ \ 3 \\ \hline 72 \end{array}$$
11
$$\begin{array}{r} 67 \\ \times \ \ 4 \\ \hline 268 \end{array}$$

4
$$\begin{array}{r} 362 \\ - 151 \\ \hline 211 \end{array}$$
8
$$\begin{array}{r} 32 \\ \times \ \ 5 \\ \hline 160 \end{array}$$
12
$$\begin{array}{r} 23 \\ \times \ \ 8 \\ \hline 184 \end{array}$$

page 126 (Test 1)

1 1238 　 4 2 　 7 28 　 10 6
2 500 　 5 45 　 8 180 　 11 4
3 175 　 6 200 　 9 58p 　 12 $\frac{3}{10}$
13 600 ml 　 17 1·7
14 3:55 p.m. 　 18 2 kg
15 £18 　 19 180°
16 8 　 20 8, 16, 24, 32, 40

page 126 (Test 2)

1 60 　 8 316 　 15 2 kg
2 5 　 9 £28 　 16 6
3 −2°C 　 10 45° 　 17 560
4 0·5 　 11 5 　 18 500 ml
5 28 　 12 2 m 40 cm 　 19 11:35
6 27 　 13 56 　 20 20
7 2076 　 14 £24

page 127 (Test 3)

1 28 　 8 180° 　 15 800
2 0·8 　 9 8 　 16 1·9
3 120 　 10 1309 　 17 2 kg
4 25p 　 11 21 　 18 3
5 30 　 12 £2 　 19 175
6 1250 m 　 13 250 ml 　 20 335 or 336
7 4756 　 14 20 cm

page 127 (Test 4)

1 45 　 11 32
2 3°C 　 12 £1·65
3 95 　 13 5007
4 75p 　 14 35 mins.
5 2500 ml 　 15 673
6 $\frac{7}{10}$ 　 16 10 o'clock
7 4 　 17 1994
8 £4 　 18 1 kg 300 g
9 4 　 19 0·25
10 1 m 40 cm 　 20 7